Preface to the Third Edit

This new edition of the long-established handbook originally written by the late Mr W. Morgan has been thoroughly revised and updated and its contents have been expanded.

In preparing this edition the authors have aimed to retain its wide appeal to students of civil engineering, architecture and building, who require as part of their studies a general introduction to accepted simplified methods of structural design in the most commonly used materials of construction.

The major changes in this edition include completely revised sections on reinforced concrete, prestressed concrete, structural timber and load-bearing masonry. This brings these sections into line with the latest recommendations of the British Standards Institution. The general section has also been expanded.

Our thanks are due to Mr John Hopkins who so expertly prepared the illustrations, to Mrs Sylvia Tomlinson for so patiently typing the manuscript and to Mr Robert Rudd for reading the proofs and making helpful suggestions.

B. G. Fletcher
S. A. Lavan

Contents

Acknowledgements

The extracts in Section 3 from CP 110 : Part 1 : 1972 and from BS 5628 : Part 1 : 1978 are reproduced by permission of the British Standards Institution, 2 Park Street, London W1A 2BS from whom complete copies of the standards may be obtained.

Details of the steel sections dimensions and properties on pages 28 to 45 have been taken from the *Structural Steelwork Handbook* and are reproduced in this publication by permission of the BRITISH CONSTRUCTIONAL STEELWORK ASSOCIATION LTD. and CONSTRADO. Copies of this complete publication, which contains the Safe Load Tables, can be obtained from the BCSA Ltd., 92–96 Vauxhall Bridge Road, London, SW1V 2RL. The copyright of these extracts belongs to the BCSA and CONSTRADO and they may not be re-copied in any form or stored in a retrieval system without their permission.

1 General

1.1 SI UNITS

The Système International d'Unités (SI) is an international system of measurement based on seven fundamental units (Table 1.1). These basic SI units can be combined in either product or quotient form to derive SI units (Table 1.2). The unit of force, the newton, is derived from the unit of mass through the relationship that force is equal to mass times the gravitational constant of 9.81 m/s^2:

e.g. 1000 kg $= 1000 \times 9.81$ kg m/s$^2 = 9810$ N

Table 1.1   Basic SI units

Quantity	Name of unit	Unit symbol
Length	metre	m
Mass	kilogram	kg
Amount of substance	mole	mol
Time	second	s
Electric current	ampere	A
Thermodynamic temperature	kelvin	K
Luminous intensity	candela	cd

Table 1.2   Some derived SI units

Quantity	Name of unit	Unit symbol
Force	newton	N
Area	square metre	m^2
Volume	cubic metre	m^3
Density	kilogram per cubic metre	kg/m^3
Pressure and stress	newton per square metre	N/m^2

A detailed description of the system of SI units is given in BS 3763: 1964, *The International System (SI) Units*. To express magnitudes of a unit, decimal multiples or submultiples are formed using a prefix with the name of the unit (Table 1.3).

Indices
It will be noted that in Table 1.3 the multiplication factor has been expressed in two ways: as a whole number and as a power of 10,

e.g. $1\,000\,000$ or 10^6

The method of expressing large or very small num-

Table 1.3   Magnitudes of SI units

Multiplication factor		Prefix	Symbol	Example
1 000 000 000	10^9	giga	G	giganewtons (GN)
1 000 000	10^6	mega	M	megawatt (MW)
1 000	10^3	kilo	k	kilometre (km)
100	10^2	hecto	h	These factors are
10	10	deca	da	non-preferred and
0·1	10^{-1}	deci	d	should be avoided
0·01	10^{-2}	centi	C	
0·001	10^{-3}	milli	m	millimetre (mm)
0·000 001	10^{-6}	micro	μ	microsecond (μs)

bers in terms of a power of 10 is of considerable use to the structural engineering student. The laws of indices are as follows:

1. $10^x = 10 \times 10 \times 10 \ldots$ to x occurrences of 10

e.g. $10^4 = 10 \times 10 \times 10 \times 10 = 10\,000$

It follows, for example, that $2\,340\,000$ can be rewritten in the convenient form 2.34×10^6.

2. The product of powers.
$$10^x \times 10^y = (10 \times 10 \times 10 \ldots \text{ to } x \text{ occurrences of } 10) \times (10 \times 10 \times 10 \ldots \text{ to } y \text{ occurrences of } 10)$$
$$= 10^{x+y}$$
e.g. $10^6 \times 10^8 = 10^{6+8} = 10^{14}$

3. The quotient of powers.
$$\frac{10^x}{10^y} = \frac{10 \times 10 \times 10 \ldots \text{ to } x \text{ occurrences of } 10}{10 \times 10 \times 10 \ldots \text{ to } y \text{ occurrences of } 10}$$
$$= 10^{x-y}$$
e.g. $10^{12}/10^9 = 10^{12-9} = 10^3$

4. The product of indices.
$$(10^x)^y = 10^{xy}$$
e.g. $(10^3)^4 = 10^{3 \times 4} = 10^{12}$
$\quad\quad (10^4)^3 = 10^{4 \times 3} = 10^{12}$

5. 10 raised to the power of zero equals 1.

i.e. $10^0 = 1$
because $10^1/10^1 = 10^{1-1} = 10^0$
But $10^1/10^1 = 1$
therefore $10^0 = 1$

6. Reciprocals.

$1/10 = 10^{-1}$
or in general terms
$1/10^x = 10^{-x}$

7. Other laws.

(a) $(10a)^x = 10^x \times a^x$

e.g. $(10 \times 14)^3 = 10^3 \times 14^3$
$= 10^3 \times 2744$
$= 10^3 \times (2 \cdot 744 \times 10^3)$
$= 2 \cdot 744 \times 10^6$

(b) $\left(\dfrac{10^x}{10^y}\right)^z = \dfrac{10^{xz}}{10^{yz}} = 10^{xz - yz}$

e.g. $\left(\dfrac{10^2}{10^5}\right)^4 = \dfrac{10^8}{10^{20}} = 10^{8-20}$
$= 10^{-12} = 1/10^{12}$

(c) $10^{1/x} = \sqrt[x]{10}$

e.g. $10^{1/3} = \sqrt[3]{10}$

(d) $10^{x/y} = \sqrt[y]{10^x}$

e.g. $10^{\frac{3}{4}} = \sqrt[4]{10^3}$

Compatibility of units

If calculations are to be successful it is imperative that quantities involved are expressed in compatible units. If, for example, it is necessary to calculate the area of a rectangle whose sides are 1·5 m and 350 mm then first the 1·5 m must be expressed in millimetres or the 350 mm in terms of metres.

The former action will give an answer where the derived unit is mm² while in the latter case the derived unit will be m². In the former case:

since $1 \text{ m} = 10^3 \text{ mm}$
area $= 1 \cdot 5 \times 10^3 \times 350 = 525 \times 10^3 \text{ mm}^2$
$= 525\,000 \text{ mm}^2$

In the latter case:

from $1 \text{ m} = 10^3 \text{ mm}$
$1 \text{ mm} = 1/10^3 \text{ m} = 10^{-3} \text{ m}$
hence area $= 1 \cdot 5 \times (350 \times 10^{-3}) = 525 \times 10^{-3} \text{ m}^2$
$= 0 \cdot 525 \text{ m}^2$

To convert kN m to N mm:

$1 \text{ kN} = 10^3 \text{ N}$ $\qquad 1 \text{ m} = 10^3 \text{ mm}$
hence $1 \text{ kN m} = (10^3 \text{ N}) \times (10^3 \text{ mm}) = 10^6 \text{ N mm}$

To convert N/mm² to kN/m²:

$1 \text{ N} = 1/10^3 \text{ kN} = 10^{-3} \text{ kN}$
$1 \text{ mm} = 1/10^3 \text{ m} = 10^{-3} \text{ m}$
hence $1 \text{ mm}^2 = (10^{-3} \text{ m})^2 = 10^{-6} \text{ m}^2$

hence $\dfrac{\text{N}}{\text{mm}^2} = \dfrac{10^{-3} \text{ kN}}{10^{-6} \text{ m}^2} = 10^{-3+6} \text{ kN/m}^2$
$= 10^3 \text{ kN/m}^2$

SI notation

The decimal marker is the conventional decimal point, raised from the line, and not the comma used in some early British publications and still in use in some metric countries. The full stop on the line is used in typewriting unless the machine has a special character above the line. Values less than unity should always have a zero before the decimal point, so that we write, for example, 0·600, *not* ·600. No full stop is used for abbreviations used as symbols for units; for example, the abbreviation for millimetre is 'mm', *not* 'mm.'. Where there is a group of five or more digits to left or right of the decimal point, they are grouped in threes with a space, not a comma, dividing them; thus

0·1041	1041·0
0·104 11	11 041·0
0·104 111	111 041·0

On drawings, dimensions are always in metres or millimetres, indicated by figures only, with no symbol. A dimension in metres always has three digits after the decimal point; thus

1·740		14	
0·320	all metres	112·5	all millimetres
14·000		2741	

1.2 DEFINITIONS

Effective length of columns

See 'Slenderness ratio' (page 6).

Elasticity

A material is said to be elastic if it displays the characteristic of reverting to its original shape after an applied force, which has caused a deformation of its shape, is removed.

End fixity of beams

End fixity refers to the degree of restraint against rotation, in the plane of bending, of a beam at its end supports, when a force is applied to that beam. The two extreme conditions of end fixity are:

(a) Fully fixed end conditions, in which case the ends of the beam can resist rotation and hence bend-

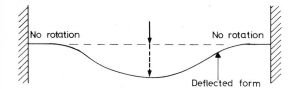

Figure 1.1 Fully fixed end conditions

ing forces. Bending moments are induced at the supports (Figure 1.1).
(b) Simply supported end conditions, in which case the ends of the beam are free to rotate, and hence cannot resist bending forces. A characteristic of a simple support is that it cannot induce a bending moment (Figure 1.2).

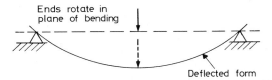

Figure 1.2 Simply supported end conditions

In practice the degree of fixity of the beam supports is somewhere between the two cases described above. It is therefore normal practice when calculating the bending moments to consider a beam as being simply supported unless the end fixity can be determined.

Factor of safety

With regard to the design of structural members etc., the factor of safety is given by

$$\frac{\text{Ultimate or failing stress}}{\text{Permissible stress}}$$

(see also 'Load factor'). For materials such as mild steel which have a definite yield point the factor of safety is sometimes taken as

$$\frac{\text{Yield stress}}{\text{Permissible stress}}$$

In overturning calculations for walls, the factor of safety against overturning is

$$\frac{\text{Stability moment}}{\text{Overturning moment}}$$

For sliding of walls the factor of safety is

$$\frac{\text{Force resisting sliding}}{\text{Force causing sliding}}$$

Force

Force is any cause which produces or tends to produce moment or change of motion in the body on which it acts. Force is measured in newtons. One newton is defined as that force which when applied to a mass of 1 kg gives that mass an acceleration of 1 m/s².

Hooke's law

This law states that the deformation in an elastic material is proportional to the load on it. As deformation can be described by strain and load can be considered in terms of stress, it can be seen that in an elastic body strain is proportional to stress.

Load factor

The load factor of a member is defined as

$$\frac{\text{Load which would cause failure}}{\text{Design load}}$$

This, of course, gives a margin of safety, but load factor is not the same as factor of safety. Load-factor design is based on the actual conditions of stress at failure, when stress is not proportional to strain. The factor of safety, applied for example to beams, is usually based on the failing (or yield) stress in tension or compression, and the beams are designed assuming elasticity.

Middle-third rule

This rule is usually employed in the design of masonry and mass concrete construction (e.g. foundations, piers and retaining walls) and applies to rectangular cross sections: in order that tensile

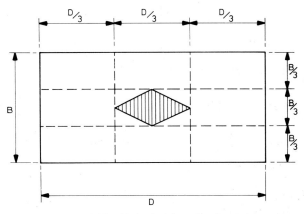

Figure 1.3 The middle-third rule (plan of a pier etc.)

stresses do not develop in the material, the resultant thrust must not be outside the kern shown shaded in Figure 1.3.

Modulus of elasticity or Young's modulus

This refers to the lengthening or shortening of members subjected to a direct force: since in an elastic material stress is proportional to strain, the ratio of stress and strain is constant. This constant is called the modulus (i.e. measure) of elasticity and is usually denoted by E. It is usually expressed in N/mm^2.

$$\frac{Stress}{Strain} = E \quad \text{or} \quad \frac{W/A}{\delta/l} = E$$

hence $E = Wl/A\delta$

where W = direct force, l = the gauge length, A = the original cross-sectional area of the member and δ = the change in length of the member.

The modulus of elasticity gives an indication of the 'stiffness' of a material. The greater the value of E, the greater is the resistance to deformation (i.e. to lengthening, shortening or bending) of the member; that is, a big stress is required to produce a small strain.

The modulus of elasticity must not be confused with the 'elastic modulus', which is used in certain steelwork tables in place of 'section modulus' to distinguish between the elastic and plastic section moduli.

Moment of a force

The moment of a force is the turning effect or leverage of that force about a given point or axis. It is measured by multiplying the force by the perpendicular distance of its line of action from the point or axis. It is generally expressed in N mm or kN m (Figure 1.4).

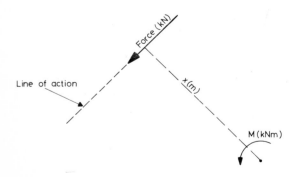

Figure 1.4   The moment of a force

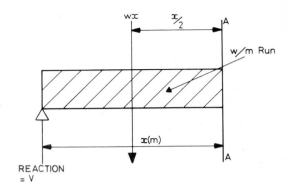

Figure 1.5   A bending moment

Moment, bending

When a member or portion of a member is so restrained or fixed that an applied moment cannot cause rotation about the point under consideration, bending is caused and the moment is then called a bending moment. With reference to Figure 1.5, the bending moment at AA is the sum of the moments of the forces acting about that point: in this case, $+ Vx - wx^2/2$

Moment of inertia

This is a term used in dynamics for rotating parts such as flywheels and armatures. A flywheel has inertia (i.e. a reluctance to having its state of rest or of motion changed) and a certain moment is required to cause it to rotate. This moment depends on the mass of the material and its arrangement with respect to the axis of rotation. The contribution of each particle of material to the total energy of the wheel depends on the mass of the particle and the square of its distance from the axis of rotation. The moment of inertia is defined as the sum of all these products taking all particles into account. This can be expressed mathematically as

$I = \Sigma my^2$

where m = the mass of a particle, y = its distance from the axis, and Σ indicates 'sum of'.

In deriving beam design formulae the expression Σay^2 is arrived at, where a is the area of a small element at a distance y from the axis of bending; because of its similarity with Σmy^2, this expression is also called the moment of inertia. However, it might be more accurate to call it the second moment of area. Referring to Figure 1.6, the second moment of area about XX is

$$I_{XX} = \Sigma ay^2$$
$$= a_1 y_1^2 + a_2 y_2^2 + a_3 y_3^2 + a_4 y_4^2 + \dots$$

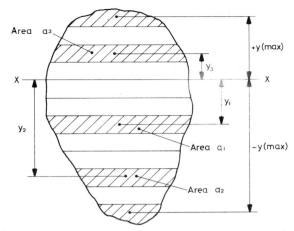

Figure 1.6 The second moment of area

For geometrical figures (rectangles, circles etc.) general formulae for ΣAy^2 or I can be found by integrating Ay^2 through the limits of $+y(\max)$ and $-y(\max)$. For symmetrical shapes, see 'Section properties'.

Moment of resistance

The bending moment of a beam must be resisted by an internal moment set up by the action of the beam fibres. The maximum bending moment M depends on the loads and reactions. The maximum safe moment of resistance M_r that a beam can supply depends on the maximum permissible stress σ for the material and the size and shape of the cross section (i.e. the moment of inertia). Normally, for design purposes, the maximum moment of resistance M_r is made equal to the maximum bending moment M. The beam design formula is obtained from the simplified theory of bending that states

$M/I = \sigma/y$

where $M =$ the bending moment or moment of resistance, $I =$ the moment of inertia, $\sigma =$ maximum permissible bending stress and $y =$ the distance from the neutral axis to the extreme fibres of the beam.

Pinned (hinged) members

A hinge is a form of support that keeps the ends of the member in position but allows freedom to rotate. There is, therefore, no bending moment at a hinge. Depending on the disposition of the loads, the reaction at a hinge can be at any angle (see 'End fixity of beams', page 2).

Radius of gyration

This term was first used in dynamics, e.g. of flywheels. In comparing the effectiveness of such wheels, it is imagined that the mass of the wheel is concentrated into one particle at a distance from the centroid of the wheel so that the total moment of inertia is unaltered. The distance of this particle from the centre of the wheel is called the radius of gyration.

With respect to columns which are liable to buckle (bend) the radius of gyration can be thought of as the distance from the axis of bending at which the whole area of the cross section can be assumed to be concentrated so that the resistance to bending remains unaltered. The radius of gyration takes into account not only the size of the cross section but also its shape, i.e. the arrangement of the material with respect to the axis of buckling.

Usually, for design of columns, the least radius of gyration is required:

$$\text{Least radius of gyration} = \sqrt{\frac{\text{Least moment of inertia}}{\text{Area of cross section}}}$$

i.e. $r = \sqrt{I/A}$

Roller bearing

When the ends of a member are supported on rollers they are free to move longitudinally and also to rotate. The reaction at a roller bearing is always at right angles to the line of rollers (Figure 1.7).

Section modulus

The moment of resistance M_r of a homogeneous beam depends on the nature of the material and on the size and shape of its cross section. The nature of the material is provided for by the permissible stress σ and the section modulus can be defined as the size–shape factor Z:

$Z = I/y$

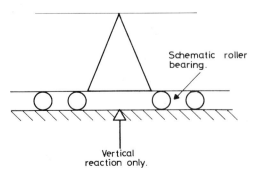

Figure 1.7 Roller bearing

where I = the moment of inertia and y = the distance from the neutral axis to extreme fibres of the beam.

Simply (freely) supported beams
See 'End fixity'.

Slenderness ratio
The slenderness ratio of a steel or timber column is usually expressed as

$$\frac{\text{Effective height of the column}}{\text{Least radius of gyration}} \quad \text{i.e.} \quad \frac{l}{r}$$

Tables of permissible stresses for posts, struts and columns are usually based on specified end conditions of the column, e.g. 'Restrained at both ends in position but not in direction' (both ends hinged). In this case the effective height l of the column equals its actual height L. For other conditions of end restraint allowance is made for the different load-carrying capacities of the column by using effective heights as given in Table 1.4. This table is common to both timber and steel columns.

Table 1.4 Effective heights for various end conditions in steel and timber columns

Condition of end restraint	Effective height l
1. Restrained at both ends in position and direction (both ends fixed)	$0.7L$
2. Restrained at both ends in position and at one end in direction (one end fixed, one end hinged)	$0.85L$
3. Restrained at both ends in position but not in direction (both ends hinged)	L
4. Restrained at one end in position and direction and at the other end partially restrained in direction but not in position	$1.5L$
5. Restrained at one end in position and direction but not restrained in either position or direction at the other end (one end fixed, one end free)	$2.0L$

The effective height of a reinforced concrete column may be determined from table in CP 110: 1972, *The structural use of concrete*. This table is based on the degree of end restraint. In addition CP 110: 1972 suggests that a more accurate estimate of the effective height may be obtained by considering the actual joint stiffness at each end.

The slenderness ratio of a reinforced concrete column is the effective height divided by the side of the column about both axes. If the ratio about both axes is 12 or less the column is considered as short; otherwise it is slender.

Stress
Stress may be thought of as the internal 'distress' of a member as a result of the application of external loads. It is the resistance set up by the particles of the member in opposition to the breaking tendency of the loads. Stress is expressed as load per unit area (W/A), e.g. N/mm^2, kN/mm^2, kN/m^2.

In simple bending $M/I = \sigma/y$
and hence $\sigma = My/I$
where M = the bending moment or moment of resistance, I = the moment of inertia, y = the distance from the neutral axis to the extreme fibre and σ = the bending stress

Strain
A member cannot be subjected to a stress without being deformed, i.e. strained. The most important strains are elongation (due to tension) and shortening (due to compression). Such strains are defined as the change δ in length divided by the original unloaded length L of the member:

$$\text{Strain} = \delta/L$$

Yield stress
This applies particularly to mild steel. If a bar of steel is subjected to a tensile force it behaves 'elastically' until a certain stress (the yield stress) is reached. The bar then stretches a great deal and becomes more or less plastic. Increased load produces larger and larger extensions until the bar finally breaks.

1.3 LOADING

Minimum imposed floor loads
CP 3 Chapter V Part 1: 1967 provides information on dead and imposed loads. All floor slabs are designed to carry the appropriate distributed or concentrated imposed loads designated in the code. Beams are to be designed to carry a distributed load appropriate to their use. If a value is not given for a concentrated load it may be assumed that the distributed load is adequate for design purposes (Table 1.5).

Reduction in total distributed imposed floor loads
If a single span of a beam supports more than $46\ m^2$ of floor at one general level, the imposed load

Table 1.5 Minimum imposed floor loads

Type of building or structure	Distributed load		Concentrated load over a 300 mm sq	
	kN/m^2	kgf/m^2	kN	kgf
Assembly buildings				
with fixed seating	4·0	408	–	–
without fixed seating	5·0	510	3·6	367
Bedrooms				
domestic buildings	1·5	153	1·4	143
hotels	2·0	204	1·8	184
institutions	1·5	153	1·8	184
Book stores	2·4 for each metre of storage height	245	7·0	714
Clubs				
assembly areas with fixed seating	4·0	408	–	–
assembly areas without fixed seating	5·0	510	3·6	367
Colleges				
classrooms	3·0	306	2·7	275
dining rooms	2·0	204	2·7	275
dormitories	1·5	153	1·8	184
gymnasia	5·0	510	3·6	367
Corridors etc. and footbridges between buildings				
subject to crowd loadings	4·0	408	4·5	459
subject to loads greater than crowds	5·0	510	4·5	459
Dance halls	5·0	510	3·6	367
Factories and similar buildings	5·0	510	4·5	459
	7·5 or 10·0	765 or 1020	6·7	683
			9·0	918
Garages				
car parking for vehicles not exceeding 2500 kg	2·5	255	9·0	918
all repair workshops and parking for vehicles				
exceeding 2500 kg	5·0	510	9·0	918
Hospitals				
wards, utility rooms	2·0	204	1·8	184
operating theatres	2·0	204	4·5	459
Hotels				
bars and vestibules	5·0	510	–	–
kitchens	3·0	306	4·5	459
Houses	1·5	153	1·4	143
Offices				
filing and storage	5·0	510	4·5	459
general	2·5	255	2·7	275
with computing equipment etc.	3·5	357	4·5	459
Stairs				
houses less than 3 stories	1·5	153	1·8	184
all other buildings — the same as the floors to which they give access	3·0–5·0	306–510		
Stationery stores	4·0 for each metre of storage height	408	9·0	918

Table 1.6   Reduction in total distributed imposed floor loads

Number of floors, including roof, carried by member	1	2	3	4	5–10	10+
Percentage reduction in load on all floors carried by member	0	10	20	30	40	50

can be reduced by 5% for each 46 m², subject to a maximum reduction of 25% (Table 1.6).

Flat roofs and sloping roofs up to 10°

If access, in addition to that needed for cleaning and repair, is to be provided, the imposed load is 1·5 kN/m² or a load of 1·8 kN/m² concentrated on a 300 mm square.

If no access is to be provided other than that required for cleaning and repair, the imposed load is 0·75 kN/m² or a load of 0·9 kN/m² concentrated on a 300 mm square.

Sloping roofs

If the slope is greater than 10° with no access provided other than that needed for cleaning and repair, the following imposed loads apply:

1. Up to 30° a load of 0·75 kN/m² measured on plan or a vertical load of 0·9 kN on a square with a 300 mm side.
2. No imposed load to be considered if the slope is greater than 75°. For slopes between 30° and 75° the imposed load is found by linear interpolation.

Horizontal loads on parapets and balustrades (Table 1.7)

Table 1.7   Horizontal loads on parapets and balustrades

Use	Intensity of horizontal load	
	N/m run	kgf/m run
Light access stairs etc. less than 600 mm wide	200	22·4
Light access stairs etc. more than 600 mm wide to private and domestic premises	360	36·7
All other stairways etc. parapets to roofs	740	75·5
Panic barriers	3000	306

Wind loading

CP 3 Chapter V Part 2: 1972 provides information on wind loads. The treatment of wind loading is now very much more complicated than in previous codes. It is therefore not possible to summarise the requirements of this code adequately, and reference must be made to the code if such information is required.

Mass densities of materials

Table 1.8   Mass densities of materials

Material	kg/m³
Aluminium	2771
Asbestos cement	1922–2082
Asphalt	2082
Bitumen roofing felt	593
Brass	8426
Brickwork, commons	2000
heavy pressed brick	2240
engineering	2400
Cement	1441
Concrete, plain	2300
reinforced	2400
Copper	8730
Cork	128–240
Felt, roofing	593
Fibre building board	160–400
Floors — hollow clay blocks with concrete ribs between blocks and 40 mm concrete topping	1600
Glass plate	2787
Lead	11 325
Plaster, acoustic	800
fibrous	430
gypsum	1920
Steel, mild	7849
Stone, limestone	2082–2243
sandstone	2195–2403
granite	2595–2931
Timber, oak	721–961
pitch-pine	673
Douglas fir	529

1.4 BENDING MOMENTS, SHEAR FORCE, DEFLECTIONS AND SECTION PROPERTIES

Maximum bending moments, shear forces and deflections (Table 1.9)

Section properties

The following symbols are used.

A = area of cross section (mm²)

y = distance from neutral axis to extreme fibres (mm) (It is this distance which is also used in expression $M/I = \sigma/y$.)

XX, and YY are axes which pass through the centroid of the section.

Table 1.9

Loading	Maximum bending moment	Maximum shear force	Maximum deflection
Point load W at mid-span, spans $L/2$, $L/2$	$\dfrac{WL}{4}$	$\dfrac{W}{2}$	$\dfrac{WL^3}{48EI}$
Two loads $W/2$ at thirds, spans $L/3$, $L/3$, $L/3$	$\dfrac{WL}{6}$	$\dfrac{W}{2}$	$\dfrac{23WL^3}{1296EI}$
Two loads $W/2$, spans $L/4$, $L/2$, $L/4$	$\dfrac{WL}{8}$	$\dfrac{W}{2}$	$\dfrac{11WL^3}{768EI}$
u.d.l $= W$, span L	$\dfrac{WL}{8}$	$\dfrac{W}{2}$	$\dfrac{5WL^3}{384EI}$
Total load $= W$ (triangular), span L	$\dfrac{WL}{6}$	$\dfrac{W}{2}$	$\dfrac{WL^3}{60EI}$
Fixed ends, point load W at mid-span, spans $L/2$, $L/2$	$\dfrac{WL}{8}$ (at supports and at mid-span)	$\dfrac{W}{2}$	$\dfrac{WL^3}{192EI}$
Cantilever, u.d.l $= W$, span L	$\dfrac{WL}{2}$	W	$\dfrac{WL^3}{8EI}$
Cantilever, point load W at end, span L	WL	W	$\dfrac{WL^3}{3EI}$
Fixed ends, u.d.l $= W$, span L	$\dfrac{WL}{12}$ at supports $\dfrac{WL}{24}$ at mid-span	$\dfrac{W}{2}$	$\dfrac{WL^3}{384EI}$

I_{XX}, I_{YY} = moments of inertia (i.e. second moments of area) about the axes XX and YY (mm⁴)

Z_{XX}, Z_{YY} = section moduli about the axes XX and YY (mm³)

r_{XX}, r_{YY} = radius of gyration about axes XX and YY (mm)

$$r = \sqrt{(I/A)}$$

Properties of a rectangle (Figure 1.8)

$A = BD \qquad y_1 = D/2$

$I_{XX} = BD^3/12$

$Z_{XX} = BD^2/6$

$r_{XX} = \sqrt{(I_{XX}/A)} = 0.289\sqrt{D}$

$y_2 = B/2$

$I_{YY} = DB^3/12$

$Z_{YY} = DB^2/6$

$r_{YY} = 0.289\sqrt{B}$

Properties of a hollow rectangle (Figure 1.9)

$A = BD - bd \qquad y_1 = D/2 \qquad y_2 = B/2$

$$I_{XX} = \frac{BD^3 - bd^3}{12} \qquad I_{YY} = \frac{DB^3 - db^3}{12}$$

$$Z_{XX} = \frac{BD^3 - bd^3}{6D} \qquad Z_{YY} = \frac{DB^3 - db^3}{6B}$$

$$r_{XX} = \sqrt{(I_{XX}/A)} \qquad r_{YY} = \sqrt{(I_{YY}/A)}$$

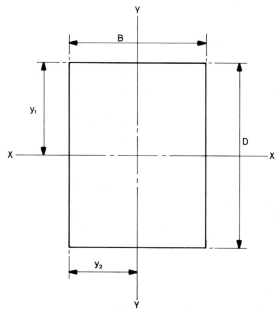

Figure 1.8 Properties of a rectangle

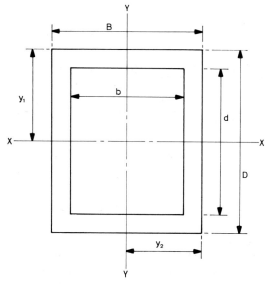

Figure 1.9 Properties of a hollow rectangle

Properties of an 'I' section (Figure 1.10)

$$A = BD - db \qquad y_1 = D/2 \qquad y_2 = B/2$$
$$I_{XX} = \frac{BD^3 - bd^3}{12} \qquad I_{YY} = \frac{2TB^3}{12} + \frac{dt^3}{12}$$
$$Z_{XX} = I_{XX} \div D/2 \qquad Z_{YY} = I_{YY} \div B/2$$
$$r_{XX} = \sqrt{(I_{XX}/A)} \qquad r_{YY} = \sqrt{(I_{YY}/A)}$$

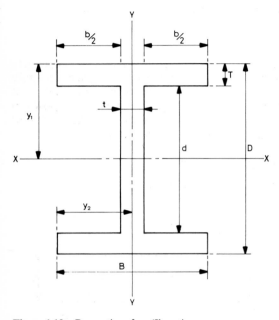

Figure 1.10   Properties of an 'I' section

Properties of a rectangle with axis on base
(Figure 1.11)

$$A = BD \qquad I_{VV} = BD^3/3$$

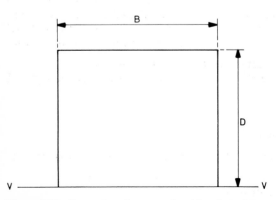

Figure 1.11   Properties of a rectangle with axis on base

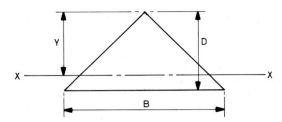

Figure 1.12   Properties of a triangle with axis through centroid

Properties of a triangle with axis through centroid
(Figure 1.12)

$$A = BD/2 \qquad\qquad y = 2D/3$$
$$I_{XX} = BD^3/36 \qquad\qquad Z_{XX} = BD^2/24$$
$$r_{XX} = D/\sqrt{18} = 0{\cdot}236D$$

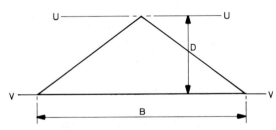

Figure 1.13   Properties of a triangle with axis on base or apex

Properties of a triangle with axis on base or apex
(Figure 1.13)

$$A = BD/2 \qquad I_{VV} = BD^3/12 \qquad I_{UU} = BD^3/4$$

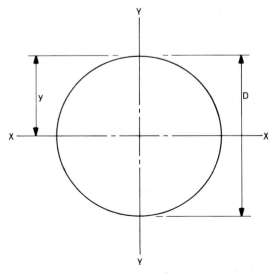

Figure 1.14   Properties of a circle with axis through centroid

Properties of a circle with axis through centroid (Figure 1.14)

$A = \pi D^2/4$ $y = D/2$
$I_{XX} = I_{YY} = \pi D^4/64$ $Z_{XX} = Z_{YY} = \pi D^3/32$
$r_{XX} = r_{YY} = D/4 = 0{\cdot}25D$

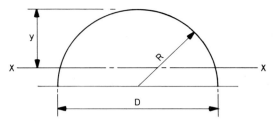

Figure 1.16   Properties of a semicircle with axis through centroid

the section. When considering an unsymmetrical section such as a flanged beam it is usual to apply the parallel axis theorem to calculate the moment of inertia. The first step, therefore, is to position these axes; the moments of inertia can then be found by using the parallel axis theorem.

Parallel axis theorem

With reference to Figure 1.17,

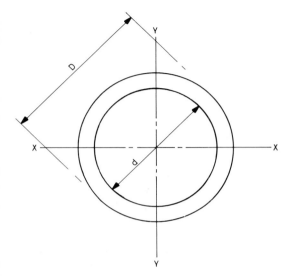

Figure 1.15   Properties of a hollow circle (i.e. ring)

Properties of a hollow circle (i.e. ring) (Figure 1.15)

$$A = \frac{\pi(D^2 - d^2)}{4} \qquad y = \frac{D}{2}$$

$$I_{XX} = I_{YY} = \frac{\pi(D^4 - d^4)}{64}$$

$$Z_{XX} = Z_{YY} = \frac{\pi(D^4 - d^4)}{32D}$$

$$r_{XX} = r_{YY} = \frac{\sqrt{(D^2 + d^2)}}{4} = 0{\cdot}25\sqrt{(D^2 + d^2)}$$

Properties of a semicircle with axis through centroid (Figure 1.16)

$$A = \frac{\pi D^2}{8} \qquad y = R\left(1 - \frac{4}{3\pi}\right)$$

$$I_{XX} = R^4\left(\frac{\pi}{8} - \frac{8}{9\pi}\right) = 0{\cdot}1093R^4$$

$$r_{XX} = \sqrt{(I_{XX}/A)} = 0{\cdot}2643R$$

Moments of inertia of unsymmetrical sections: build-up of rectangles

Usually properties such as section modulus, moment of inertia etc. are required about axes which pass through the centroid (neutral axis) of

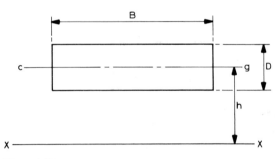

Figure 1.17

$I_{XX} = I_{cg} + Ah^2$
Where I_{XX} = the moment of inertia of the figure about XX, I_{cg} = the moment of inertia about the axis through centroid of section, A = the area of the section and h = the distance between the parallel axes. This formula is true for any shape of section.

For rectangles $I_{XX} = BD^3/12 + BDh^2$
where B is the dimension parallel to the axes cg and XX.

Example 1

Determine I_{XX} for the section shown in Figure 1.18.

Divide the section into two portions. Hence
Area of flange = A_1
Area of web = A_2

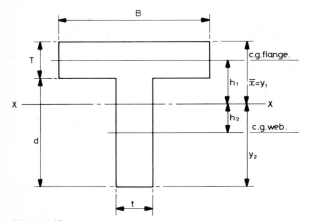

Figure 1.18

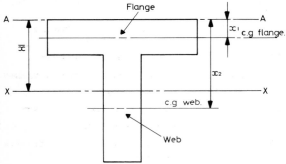

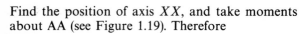

Figure 1.19

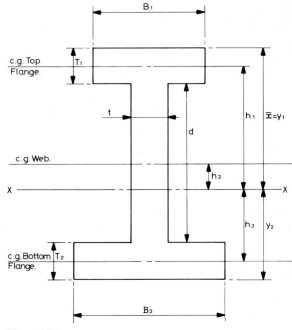

Figure 1.20

Find the position of axis XX, and take moments about AA (see Figure 1.19). Therefore

$$\bar{x} = \frac{A_1 x_1 + A_2 x_2}{A_1 + A_2}$$

I_{XX} for the section can be found by the parallel axis theorem (see Figure 1.18).

I_{XX}(flange) $= BT^3/12 + BTh_1{}^2$
I_{XX}(web $= td^3/12 + dth_2{}^2$
Total $I_{XX} = I_{XX}$(flange) $+ I_{XX}$(web)

Example 2

Determine I_{XX} for the section shown in Figure 1.20. Divide the section into three portions, i.e.

Area of top flange $= A_1$
Area of web $= A_2$
Area of bottom flange $= A_3$

Find the position of axis XX, and take moments about AA (see Figure 1.21). Therefore

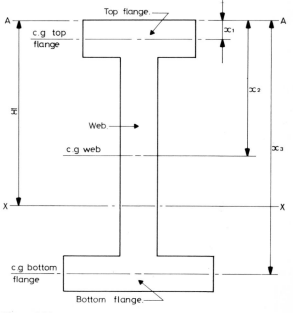

Figure 1.21

$$\bar{x} = \frac{A_1 x_1 + A_2 x_2 + A_3 x_3}{A_1 + A_2 + A_3}$$

I_{xx} for the section can be found by the parallel axis theorem (see Figure 1.20).

I_{xx}(top flange) $= B_1 T_1^3/12 + B_1 T_1 h_1^2$
I_{xx}(web) $= td^3/12 + dth_2^2$
I_{xx}(bottom flange) $= B_2 T_2^3/12 + B_2 T_2 h_3^2$
Total $I_{xx} = I_{xx}$(top flange $+ I_{xx}$(web) $+$
$\qquad\qquad I_{xx}$(bottom flange)

Section modulus of unsymmetrical sections

When it is necessary to determine the section modulus Z_{xx} for an unsymmetrical shape such as that shown in Figure 1.18 it will be noted that two values are obtained:

(i) $\quad Z_{xx} = I_{xx}/y_1 \quad$ and
(ii) $\quad Z_{xx} = I_{xx}/y_2$

For simple beam design it is usual to use the least value of Z_{xx}, which in this case will be (ii).

1.5 BRITISH STANDARDS AND CODES OF PRACTICE (Table 1.10)

A list of useful British Standards and Codes of Practice is given in Table 1.10.

Table 1.10

Number	Title
CP 3 Chapter V Part 1: 1967	Loading—Dead and imposed loads
CP 3 Chapter V Part 2: 1972	Loading—Wind loads
CP 102: 1973	Protection of buildings against water from the ground
CP 110 Part 1: 1972	Structural use of concrete—Design, materials and workmanship
CP 110 Part 2: 1972	Structural use of concrete—Design charts
CP 110 Part 3: 1972	Structural use of concrete—Design charts
CP 111: 1970	Structural recommendations for load-bearing walls
CP 112: 1967	The structural use of timber
CP 117 Part 1: 1965	Simply supported beams in building
CP 117 Part 2: 1967	Beams for bridges
CP 118: 1969	The structural use of aluminium
CP 121 Part 1: 1973	Walling—Brick and block masonry
CP 297: 1972	Precast concrete cladding (non-load bearing)
CP 301: 1971	Building drainage
CP 2004: 1972	Foundations
CP 2005: 1968	Sewerage
BS 449 Part 2: 1969	The use of structural steel in building (Metric units)
BS 648: 1964	Schedule of weights of building materials
BS 4978: 1973	Timber grades for structural use
BS 5337: 1976	Code of practice for the structural use of concrete for retaining aqueous liquids
BS 5628 Part 1: 1978	Structural use of masonry— Unreinforced masonry
BS 6031: 1981	Earthworks

2 Structural steelwork

The code for the design of structural steelwork is BS 449 Part 2: 1969, *The Use of Structural Steel in Building*. This code is at present under review.

The dimensions and properties of universal beams and columns are given in tables obtained from the British Constructional Steelwork Association.

2.1 BEAMS WITH LATERAL SUPPORT

A beam is said to be laterally supported when the compression flange is restrained from buckling by virtue of the lateral support given by floors or other beams. There would be no need to consider buckling for the beam shown in Figure 2.1(a), and the frictional resistance between the slab and the compression flange of the beam in Figure 2.1(b) is usually considered to be sufficient to eliminate the need for sideways buckling calculations.

Simple design

In the 'simple' method of design referred to in BS 449 Part 2: 1969, beams connected to columns or other beams by simple angle cleats and brackets are assumed to be simply supported for the calculation of bending moments.

Design of beams with lateral support

p_{bc} = permissible stress in compression due to bending (see Table 2.1).

Table 2.1 Allowable stress p_{bc} in bending

Section	Grade*	Thickness of material	p_{bc} (N/mm²)
Rolled 'I' beams and channels	43	All	165
Plates, angles, tees	43	≤40 mm	165
		>40 mm	150
Universal beams and columns	43	≤40 mm	165
		>40 mm	150

* Values for other grades are given in BS 449 Part 2: 1969.

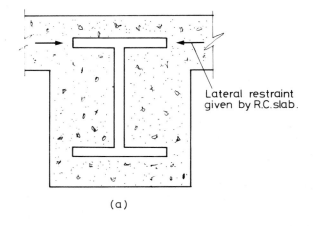

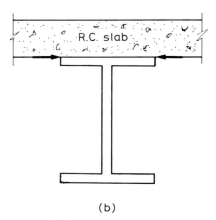

Figure 2.1 Beams with lateral support (R.C., reinforced concrete)

1. Estimate the load on the beam, including if necessary an allowance for the weight of the beam and its concrete casing (if any).
2. Calculate the maximum bending moment M in N mm.
3. Calculate the required section modulus $Z = M/p_{bc}$.

Reference is now made to the column headed 'Section modulus of XX axis' in the table of standard properties (see Table 2.8). A Z_{XX} value that is slightly greater than the calculated value is chosen. The section to which the chosen Z value

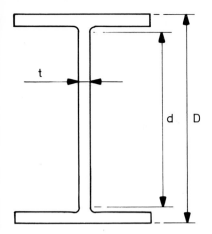

Figure 2.2

applies is the section required to resist the calculated maximum bending moment by limiting the bending stress to within the allowable stress in bending (for many students this is the final answer but checks for shear, buckling and deflection may be needed).

4. Shear.

Average shear stress = (shear force)/Dt

(see Figure 2.2). This calculated shear stress should not exceed 115 N/mm² for grade 43 steel of thickness up to and including 40 mm or 105 N/mm² for grade 43 steel greater than 40 mm thick.

5. Buckling in Figure 2.2 t = the web thickness and d = the clear depth of web between root fillets. The 45° lines are taken from the outside edge of the stiff portion of the bearing (see Figure 2.3). Bearing stiffeners are required at points of concentrated load

and at supports when the concentrated load or reaction exceeds $p_c tB$, where p_c = the axial stress for struts with a slenderness ratio of $(d/t)\sqrt{3}$ (see Table 2.4).

6. Deflection. The maximum allowable deflection should not exceed 1/360 of the span due to loads other than the self-weight of the structural floors or roof steelwork and casing. If the beam carries a uniformly distributed (U.D.) load this requirement is satisfied if the span/depth ratio for sections of grade 43 steel does not exceed the values in Table 2.2

Table 2.2   Deflection coefficients

W_d/W_t	1·0	0·90	0·80	0·70	0·6	0·5
Span/depth	16·97	18·86	21·21	24·24	28·28	33·94

W_d = load considered for deflection purposes.
W_t = total load.

2.2 BEAMS WITHOUT LATERAL SUPPORT

Examples of beams without lateral support, where the compression flange is not restrained from buckling, are given in Figure 2.4. The permissible stress depends on the ratios D/T and l/r_Y where l = the effective length of the compression flange and r_Y = the radius of gyration about axis YY.

The effective lengths l for two simple types of connection are given in Figure 2.5. When l/r_Y does not exceed 85 for grade 43 steel the stresses given in Table 2.3 for beams with lateral support may be used. Table 2.3 gives permissible stresses for grade 43 steel only. See BS 449 Part 2: 1969 for similar tables for other grades.

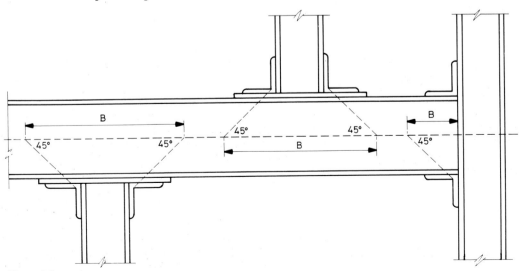

Figure 2.3

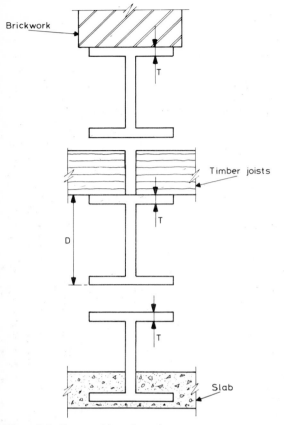

Brickwork

Timber joists

D

T

Slab

Figure 2.4   Beams without lateral support

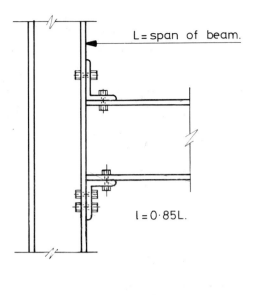

L = span of beam.

l = 0·85L.

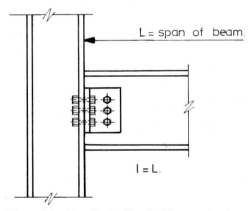

L = span of beam.

l = L.

Figure 2.5   The effective lengths *l* for two simple types of connection

Design of beams without lateral support

1. Choose a trial beam section from the tables and read off the values Z_{XX}, D/T and r_Y. Convert the values to millimetres and calculate l/r_Y.
2. From Table 2.3 read off the permissible stress p_{bc} and calculate the moment of resistance M_r of the beam from $M_r = p_{bc}Z_{XX}$.
3. Calculate the maximum bending moment M due to the imposed dead and live loads. If M_r is equal to or not much greater than M, the beam section selected is suitable for bending. If the beam section is not suitable, choose another section and repeat the calculations.
4. If necessary, check for shear, buckling and deflection as previously described.

2.3   CASED BEAMS

r_Y may be taken as $0·2 (B + 100 \text{ mm})$. D/T is the same as for an uncased section. The permissible bending stress obtained from Table 2.3 must not exceed $1\frac{1}{2}$ times that permitted for an uncased section. It should also not exceed the maximum permissible stress given in Table 2.1 for beams with lateral support. Figure 2.6 shows the requirements for a cased beam.

2.4   COLUMNS, STANCHIONS AND STRUTS

Table 2.4 gives the permissible stresses for grade 43 steel where p_c the permissible axial stress in compression on the gross cross section (N/mm²), $l =$ the

Table 2.3 Allowable stress p_{bc} in bending (N/mm²) for beams of grade 43 steel

l/r_Y	D/T							
	10	*15*	*20*	*25*	*30*	*35*	*40*	*50*
90	165	165	165	165	165	165	165	165
95	165	165	165	163	163	163	163	163
100	165	165	165	157	157	157	157	157
105	165	165	160	152	152	152	152	152
110	165	165	156	147	147	147	147	147
115	165	165	152	141	141	141	141	141
120	165	162	148	136	136	136	136	136
130	165	155	139	126	126	126	126	126
140	165	149	130	115	115	115	115	115
150	165	143	122	104	104	104	104	104
160	163	136	113	95	94	94	94	94
170	159	130	104	91	85	82	82	82
180	155	124	96	87	80	76	72	71
190	151	118	93	83	77	72	68	62
200	147	111	89	80	73	68	64	59
210	143	105	87	77	70	65	61	55
220	139	99	84	74	67	62	58	52
230	134	95	81	71	64	59	55	49
240	130	92	78	69	61	56	52	47
250	126	90	76	66	59	54	50	44
260	122	88	74	64	57	52	48	42
270	118	86	72	62	55	50	46	40
280	114	84	70	60	53	48	44	39
290	110	82	68	58	51	46	42	37
300	106	80	66	56	49	44	41	36

Intermediate values may be obtained by linear interpolation.
NOTE. For materials over 40 mm thick the stress shall not exceed 150 N/mm².

Table 2.4 Allowable stress p_c on gross section for axial compression

l/r	p_c (N/mm²) for grade 43 steel									
	0	*1*	*2*	*3*	*4*	*5*	*6*	*7*	*8*	*9*
0	155	155	154	154	153	153	153	152	152	151
10	151	151	150	150	149	149	148	148	148	147
20	147	146	146	146	145	145	144	144	144	143
30	143	142	142	142	141	141	141	140	140	139
40	139	138	138	137	137	136	136	136	135	134
50	133	133	132	131	130	130	129	128	127	126
60	126	125	124	123	122	121	120	119	118	117
70	115	114	113	112	111	110	108	107	106	105
80	104	102	101	100	99	97	96	95	94	92
90	91	90	89	87	86	85	84	83	81	80
100	79	78	77	76	75	74	73	72	71	70
110	69	68	67	66	65	64	63	62	61	61
120	60	59	58	57	56	56	55	54	53	53
130	52	51	51	50	49	49	48	48	47	46
140	46	45	45	44	43	43	42	42	41	41
150	40	40	39	39	38	38	38	37	37	36
160	36	35	35	35	34	34	33	33	33	32
170	32	32	31	31	31	30	30	30	29	29
180	29	28	28	28	28	27	27	27	26	26
190	26	26	25	25	25	25	24	24	24	24
200	24	23	23	23	23	22	22	22	22	22
210	21	21	21	21	21	20	20	20	20	20
220	20	19	19	19	19	19	19	18	18	18
230	18	18	18	18	17	17	17	17	17	17
240	17	16	16	16	16	16	16	16	16	15
250	15									
300	11									
350	8									

Intermediate values may be obtained by linear interpolation.
NOTE. For material over 40 mm thick, other than rolled 'I' beams or channels, and for universal columns of thickness exceeding 40 mm, the limiting stress is 140 N/mm².

Table 2.5 Maximum slenderness ratio of columns and struts

For any member carrying dead loads with or without imposed loads	180
For any member carrying loads resulting from wind forces only	250
For any member normally acting as a tie in a roof truss but subject to reversal of stress resulting from the action of wind	350

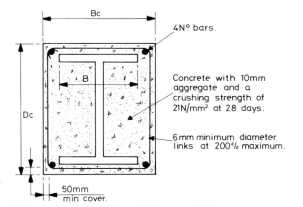

Figure 2.6 The requirements for a cased beam

Bc

4N° bars.

Concrete with 10mm aggregate and a crushing strength of 21N/mm² at 28 days.

6 mm minimum diameter links at 200°/₆ maximum.

B

Dc

50mm min cover.

effective height in mm (see Table 1.4) and r = the appropriate radius of gyration (usually the least radius of gyration, which for 'I' sections is r_Y) in mm. Stresses for other grades are given in BS 449 Part 2: 1969.

Axial loads on columns

To design an uncased universal column to carry a known axial load:

1. Choose a trial section from tables and read off its area A and least radius of gyration r_Y. Convert these values to mm² and mm.
2. Calculate the slenderness ratio l/r_Y where l = the effective height of the column in mm (see Table 2.5).
3. From Table 2.4 read off the appropriate safe axial stress p_c.
4. The safe axial load = $p_c A$. If this load is less or appreciably greater than the design load, choose another section and repeat calculations.

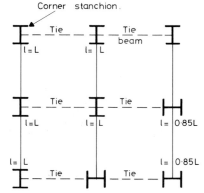

l = effective height.
L = actual height.

Figure 2.7   A rough practical guide for obtaining effective heights

Note: The effective height can be obtained from consideration of Table 1.4. A rough practical guide is given in Figure 2.7.

Design of a solid round steel column for an axial load
Proceed as above for a universal uncased column except that $r_Y = D/4$ and $A = \pi D^2/4$ where $D =$ the diameter of the column.

Design of an axially loaded cased stanchion
r_Y may be taken as $0.2\,(B + 100\text{ mm})$, the slenderness ratio $= l/r_Y$ and

$$\text{safe axial load} = p_c A + \frac{p_c}{0.19 p_{bc}} B_c D_c$$

where $A =$ the area of the steel column section and $B_c D_c =$ the overall cross-sectional area (cover in excess of 75 mm to be ignored). The safe axial load obtained must not exceed twice that which would

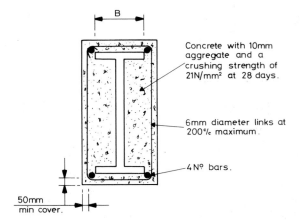

Figure 2.8   The requirements for a cased stanchion

be permitted on the uncased section. The above formula applies to mild steel sections. For cased stanchions of high-yield steel see BS 449 Part 2: 1969 and amendments. The overall dimensions of the casing should not exceed 500 mm × 1000 mm. Figure 2.8 shows the requirements for a cased stanchion.

Eccentric loading on universal columns
The amount of eccentricity to be assumed for some typical connections is given in Figure 2.9. For continuous columns (such as multistorey buildings) the bending moments due to eccentricities of loading at any one floor may be taken as being ineffective at the floors above and below that floor. The bending moments at any floor level can be equally divided between the column above and below the floor. The ratio K_1/K_2 (or K_2/K_1) of their stiffnesses

$$K = \frac{I}{L} = \frac{\text{Moment of inertia}}{\text{Actual length of column}}$$

should not exceed 1·5. Where the ratio exceeds 1·5 the bending moments are to be divided in proportion to the ratio of the K values.

Design of an intermediate length of a continuous universal column
Refer to Figure 2.10 where a column length marked ① is to be designed.

1. Choose a trial section.
2. Calculate the slenderness ratio l/r_Y and read off the permissible stress p_c from Table 2.4.
3. Add together all the loads, including the eccentric loads at the floor level Ⓕ and the loads from the

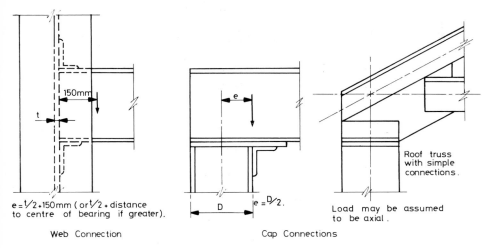

e = ¹/₂ +150mm (or ¹/₂ + distance to centre of bearing if greater).

Web Connection

e = ᴰ/₂.

Cap Connections

Roof truss with simple connections.

Load may be assumed to be axial.

Figure 2.9 The amount of eccentricity for some typical joints

floors above. Calculate the direct axial compressive stress

$$f_c = \frac{\text{Total load}}{\text{Area of column cross section}}$$

4. Calculate the maximum compression stress f_{bc} dur to the eccentric loads at floor level Ⓕ. Make allowance for the division of bending moments between the column being designed (①) and the next length above (②). Two examples are given below.

5. The column is safe if

$$\frac{\text{Actual direct stress}}{\text{Permissible direct stress}} + \frac{\text{Actual bending stress}}{\text{Permissible bending stress}}$$

does not exceed unity,

i.e. if $f_c/p_c + f_{bc}/p_{bc}$ does not exceed 1.

Example 1

Refer to Figure 2.11. It is assumed that the section is an intermediate length in a multistorey column.

1. Choose a trial section (see Table 2.10).
2. Calculate l/r_Y and obtain p_c.
3. Direct stress $= f_c = \dfrac{W + W_X + W_Y}{A}$

where A = the area of column cross section.

$M_{XX} = 0 \cdot 5 W_X e_X$ if K_1/K_2 does not exceed 1.5

$\quad\quad = W_X e_X \dfrac{K_1}{K_1 + K_2}$ if the K ratio exceeds 1.5

$M_{YY} = 0 \cdot 5 W_Y e_Y$ if K_1/K_2 does not exceed 1·5

$\quad\quad = W_Y e_Y \dfrac{K_1}{K_1 + K_2}$ if the K ratio exceeds 1·5

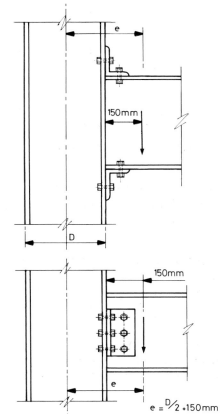

e = ᴰ/₂ +150mm

(If centre of bearing is more than 150 mm from face of stanchion, e = ᴰ/₂ + distance to centre of bearing).

Flange Connections.

Figure 2.9 (*continued*)

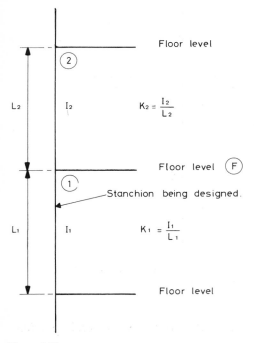

Figure 2.10

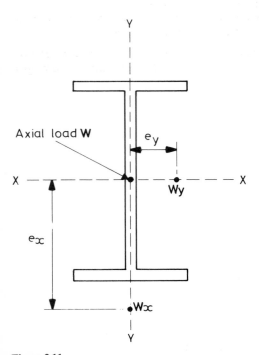

Figure 2.11

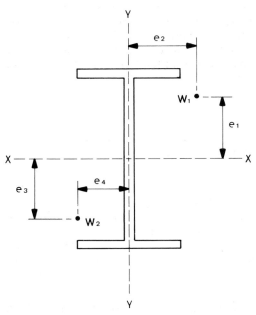

Figure 2.12

4. The maximum compressive stress due to bending

$f_{bc} = M_{XX}/Z_{XX} + M_{YY}/Z_{YY}$

The column is safe if $f_c/p_c + f_{bc}/p_{bc}$ does not exceed 1.

Example 2
Refer to Figure 2.12. It is assumed that the section is the top length supporting a roof. All the bending moments are therefore taken by this length.

1. Choose a trial section (see Table 2.10).
2. Calculate l/r_Y and obtain p_c.
3. Direct stress $= f_c = \dfrac{W_1 + W_2}{A}$

where $A =$ the area of column cross section.
$M_{XX} = W_1 e_1 - W_2 e_3$ assuming $W_1 e_1$ is greater than $W_2 e_3$
$M_{YY} = W_1 e_2 - W_2 e_4$ assuming $W_1 e_2$ is greater than $W_2 e_4$
4. The maximum compressive stress due to bending
$f_{bc} = M_{XX}/Z_{XX} + M_{YY}/Z_{YY}$

The column is safe if $f_c/p_c + f_{bc}/p_{bc}$ does not exceed 1.

Design of a cased stanchion subjected to eccentric loading

Bending moments due to eccentric loading are deemed to be taken by the steel core alone. r_Y may be taken as $0.2\,(B + 100\text{ mm})$, the slenderness ratio

$= l/r_Y$ and safe axial load $= p_c A + \dfrac{p_c}{0.19 p_{bc}} B_c D_c$

1. Choose a trial section (see Table 2.10).
2. Calculate the slenderness ratio l/r_Y and read off the permissible stress p_c from Table 2.4.
3. Add together all the loads including the eccentric loads, giving the total load W_t. Calculate the safe axial load

$$W_a = p_c A + \frac{p_c}{0.19 p_{bc}} B_c D_c$$

4. Calculate f_{bc} as for a universal column.
5. The stanchion is safe if $W_t/W_a + f_{bc}/p_{bc}$ does not exceed 1.

Angles as struts

A single angle may be classified as a discontinuous axially loaded strut when it is connected to a gusset or a section by at least two bolts in line along the angle at each end, or by their equivalent in welding (Figure 2.13).

Design of an angle as an axially loaded member

1. Choose a trial section.
2. Calculate the slenderness ratio l/r and read off the permissible stress p_c from Table 2.4 where $l = 0.85$ times the length of the angle from centre to centre of the intersections at each end and $r =$ the minimum radius of gyration.
3. Calculate the safe load $p_c A$ where $A =$ the area of cross section of the angle.

Two angles back to back may be classified as a discontinuous axially loaded strut when they are connected to both sides of a gusset or section by at least two bolts in line along the angles at each end, or by their equivalent in welding (Figure 2.14).

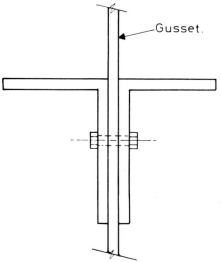

Figure 2.14 A discontinuous axially loaded strut (two angles back to back)

Design of a double angle as an axially loaded member

1. Choose a trial section.
2. Calculate the slenderness ratio l/r and read off the permissible stress p_c from Table 2.4 where $l = 0.70$–0.85 times the length of angle between intersections, depending on the degree of restraint, and $r =$ the minimum radius of gyration.
3. Calculate the safe load $p_c A$ where $A =$ the area of cross section of the two angles.

Solid washers or packings must be used at not less than two places spaced equidistant in the length of the strut.

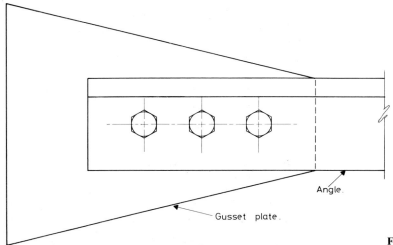

Figure 2.13

2.5 ANGLES IN TENSION

Design of a single angle
1. Choose a trial section (Figure 2.15).
2. Determine the effective area A for calculation of tensile strength, where

$$A = a_1 + a_2\frac{3a_1}{3a_1 + a_2}$$

a_1 = net sectional area of the connecting leg
    $= t(d_1 - t/2)$ — area of bolt hole

a_2 = sectional area of the unconnected leg
    $= t(d_2 - t/2)$

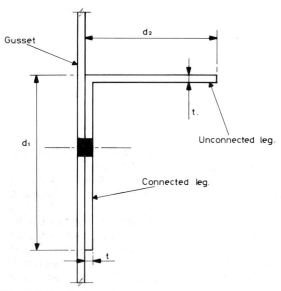

Figure 2.15   Single angle

3. Calculate the safe tensile load $p_t A$ where $p_t = 155$ N/mm² for grade 43 steel sections and 140 N/mm² for sections over 40 mm thick.

Design of a double angle
1. Choose a trial section (Figure 2.16).
2. Determine effective area A for calculation of tensile stress, where A = the gross area of the two angles minus the area of the bolt hole.
3. Calculate the safe tensile load $p_t A$.

2.6 BOLTS

Bolting is one method by which structural steel members can be connected together. Black bolds and high-strength friction grip bolts are the types in common use. Only black bolts are considered in this handbook.

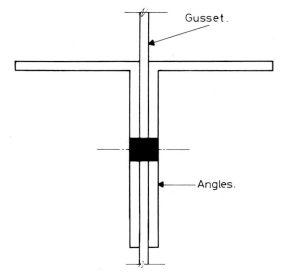

Figure 2.16   Double angle

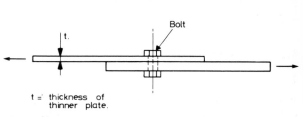

Figure 2.17   Single shear

Single shear (Figure 2.17)
The single shear value (S.S.V.) of one bolt $= f_s A$
where

A = gross area $= \pi d^2/4$ where
d = gross diameter of bolt.
f_s = allowable shear stress in bolt (see Table 2.6).

The bearing value (B.V.) of one bolt $= 0.8\, f_b dt$
where

f_b = allowable bearing stress (see Table 2.6).
d = gross diameter of bolt.
t = thickness of thinner plate.

Table 2.6   Allowable stresses in black bolts in N/mm² on gross areas

Description	Bolts of strength grade designation	
	4·6	*8·8*
In shear: black bolts	80	187
In bearing: black bolts	250	250

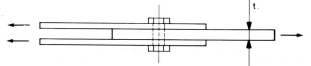

Figure 2.18 Double shear

Double shear (Figure 2.18)

The double shear value (D.S.V.) of one bolt = $2f_sA$
The bearing value (B.V.) of one bolt = f_bdt

Beam to column connections

W = load from end of beam which is assumed to be resisted entirely by bolts in the vertical leg of the seating bracket.

$$\text{Number of bolts required} = \frac{W}{\text{Safe load of one bolt}}$$

Usually the safe load for one bolt in these connections is the S.S.V. Use the B.V., however, in the flange or web if it is less than the shear value (see Figure 2.19).

Beam-to-beam connections

Example 1

Referring to Figure 2.20, V = the reaction at the end of beam B. The number of bolts required in the web of beam A is

$$\frac{V}{\text{Safe load for one bolt in shear (or bearing)}}$$

Ignoring eccentricity, the number of bolts required in the web of beam B is

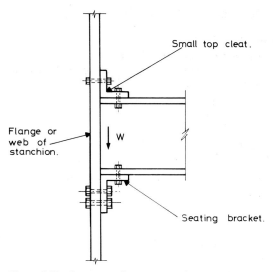

Figure 2.19 Beam-to-column connection

$$\frac{V}{\text{Safe load for one bolt}}$$

where the safe load is the lesser of the D.S.V. of one bolt or bearing in the web of beam B.

If eccentricity is taken into account, assume a number of bolts and let a be the distance of the bolt furthest away from the centre of gravity of the bolt group; b, c, d etc. are the distances of the other bolts from the centre of gravity. The vertical load on each bolt = V/N, where N = the number of bolts. Let H be the horizontal force on the highest-stressed bolt due to the moment Ve, where V = the reaction at

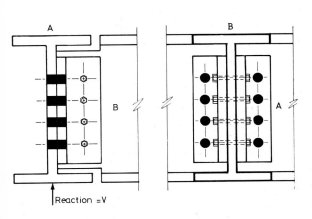

Figure 2.20 Beam-to-beam connection

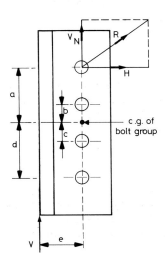

the end of beam B and e = the eccentricity of the bolt group. Then

$$\frac{H(a^2 + b^2 + c^2 + d^2 + \dots)}{a} = Ve$$

This gives a value for H. The resultant force acting on the highest stressed bolt is

$$\sqrt{[(V/N)^2 + H^2]}$$

This force must not exceed the safe load for one bolt in double shear or bearing, whichever is the lesser.

Example 2

Referring to Figure 2.21, V = the reaction at the end of beam B. The number of bolts in the web of beam A is

$$\frac{V}{\text{Safe load for one bolt in shear (or bearing)}}$$

Ignoring eccentricity, the number of bolts required in the web of beam B is

$$\frac{V}{\text{Safe load for one bolt}}$$

where the safe load is the lesser of the double shear of one bolt or bearing in the web of beam B.

If eccentricity is taken into account, assume a grouping of bolts for web B. Calculate the position of the centre of gravity of the group, and the distances a, b, c etc. from the centre of gravity. The vertical force on each bolt = V/N where N = the number of bolts. The force on each bolt due to the moment Ve will be at right angles to the line joining the bolt to the centre of gravity of the group. Let H be the force due to the moment on the bolt furthest away (distance a) from the centre of gravity.

(The forces on the other bolts will be Hb/a, Hc/a etc.) Then

$$\frac{H(a^2 + b^2 + c^2 + d^2 + e^2)}{a} = Ve_1$$

This gives a value for H. The resultant force (R_1, R_2 etc.) on each bolt can be obtained by the parallelogram of forces as shown in Figure 2.21. The resultant force on the highest-stressed bolt must not exceed the safe load for one bolt in double shear or bearing, whichever is the lesser.

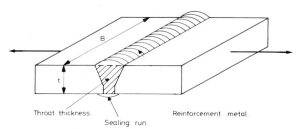

Figure 2.22   A butt weld

2.7 WELDS

Butt welds

Butt welds with reinforcement and sealing run can be treated as parent metal with a thickness equal to the throat thickness (Figure 2.22). The permissible stresses are then equal to those for the parent metal. If the plate shown in Figure 2.22 is in tension then the safe load is $p_t A$, where p_t = the permissible stresss in butt welds (see above) and A = the cross-sectional area of the plate = Bt.

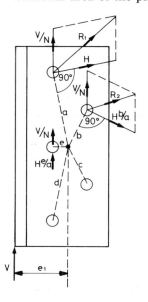

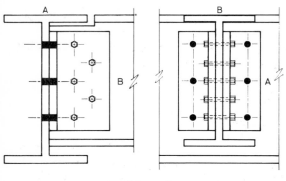

e₁ = distance from c.g. of bolt group to reaction V

Figure 2.21   Beam-to-beam connection

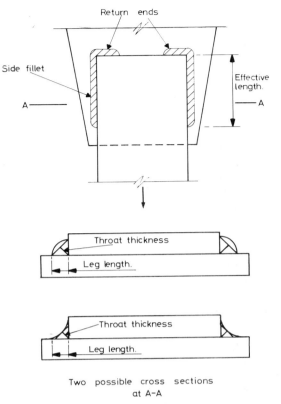

Figure 2.23   Right-angle fillet welds

Fillet welds

The permissible stress for grade 43 steel = 115 N/mm².

For right-angle welds as shown in Figure 2.23 the throat thickness = 0·7 × leg length (or length of shorter leg if the legs are unequal).

The permissible load for a one millimetre run of right-angle weld = 0·7 × (leg length) × 115 N/mm² = 80·5 × leg length (N) (see Table 2.7).

Table 2.7   Strength of fillet welds per millimetre run at 115 N/mm²

Leg length (mm)	Throat thickness (mm)	Load at 115 N/mm² (kN/mm)
3	2·1	0·24
4	2·8	0·32
5	3·5	0·40
6	4·2	0·48
8	5·6	0·64
10	7·0	0·80
12	8·4	0·97
15	10·5	1·21
18	12·6	1·45
20	14·0	1·61
22	15·4	1·71
25	17·5	2·01

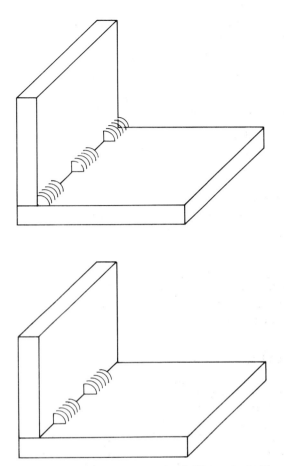

Figure 2.24   The arrangement of typical intermittent fillet welds

The permissible load for a complete run of fillet weld = 80·5 × (leg length) × (effective length of weld in mm) (N).

The effective length of fillet welds can be either
(a) The actual length of weld (if return ends of at least twice the leg length are provided).
(b) The actual length of weld minus twice the leg length (if return ends are not provided).

The arrangement of typical intermittent fillet welds is shown in Figure 2.24.

2.8 BASES

Gusset bases

Refer to Figure 2.25.

For columns with axial loads where all parts are fabricated flush for bearing (approximate method):
1. The number of bolts in the flanges of the column is

$$\frac{0·6W}{\text{Safe load for one bolt}}$$

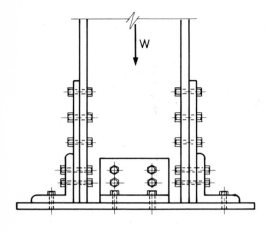

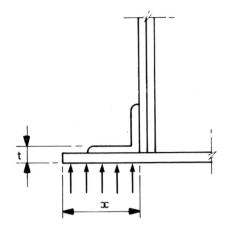

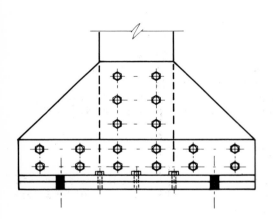

Figure 2.25   A gusset base

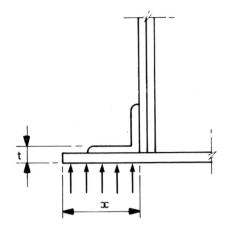

Figure 2.26

Usually the safe load for one bolt in these connections is the S.S.V. Use the B.V., however, in the flange or gusset plate if it is less than the shear value. $0.6W = 60\%$ of the axial load on the column.

2. The minimum area of the base plate is

$$\frac{W}{\text{Permissible pressure on concrete foundation}}$$

3. The thickness of the base plate (Figure 2.26).

t = combined thickness of base plate and angle.
$L_1 L_2$ = area of base.

The upthrust on the shaded area is

$$\frac{W}{L_1 L_2} \times L_1 x = \frac{Wx}{L_2}$$

The bending moment $M = Wx^2/2L_2$

$$t = \sqrt{\left(\frac{6Wx^2}{2L_1 L_2 p_{\text{bct}}}\right)}$$

W = axial column load (N).
p_{cbt} = permissible bending stress = 185 N/mm^2.

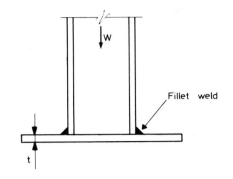

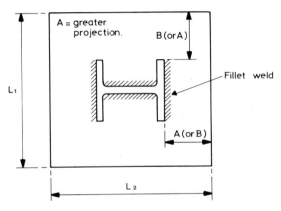

Figure 2.27   A slab base

Slab bases
Refer to Figure 2.27.

$$t = \sqrt{\left[\frac{3w}{p_{bct}}\left(A^2 - \frac{B^2}{4}\right)\right]}\ \text{where}$$

t = slab thickness (mm).
A = greater projection (mm).
B = lesser projection (mm).
$w = W/L_1 L_2$ N/mm^2.
W = axial column load (N).
p_{bct} = permissible bending stress = 185 N/mm^2.

Slab bases for solid round columns
Refer to Figure 2.28.

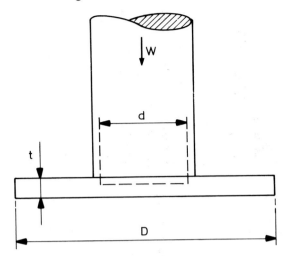

Figure 2.28   A slab base for a solid round column

$$t = \sqrt{\left(\frac{9W}{16p_{bct}}\frac{D}{D-d}\right)}\ \text{where}$$

t = slab thickness (mm).
W = axial column load (N).
D = length of side of square base (mm).
d = diameter of column
   = diameter of reduced end, if any (mm).
p_{bct} = permissible bending stress = 185 N/mm^2.

2.9 SECTION PROPERTIES

Tables 2.8–2.15 give the properties of some steel sections. Further details and safe load tables are given in the BCSA Handbook.

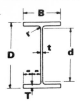

UNIVERSAL BEAMS

DIMENSIONS AND PROPERTIES

Serial size	Mass per metre	Depth of section D	Width of section B	Thickness		Root radius r	Depth between fillets d	Area of section
				Web t	Flange T			
mm	kg	mm	mm	mm	mm	mm	mm	cm²
914 × 419	388	920.5	420.5	21.5	36.6	24.1	791.4	493.9
	343	911.4	418.5	19.4	32.0	24.1	791.4	436.9
914 × 305	289	926.6	307.8	19.6	32.0	19.1	819.1	368.5
	253	918.5	305.5	17.3	27.9	19.1	819.1	322.5
	224	910.3	304.1	15.9	23.9	19.1	819.1	284.9
	201	903.0	303.4	15.2	20.2	19.1	819.1	256.1
838 × 292	226	850.9	293.8	16.1	26.8	17.8	756.5	288.4
	194	840.7	292.4	14.7	21.7	17.8	756.5	246.9
	176	834.9	291.6	14.0	18.8	17.8	756.5	223.8
762 × 267	197	769.6	268.0	15.6	25.4	16.5	681.0	250.5
	173	762.0	266.7	14.3	21.6	16.5	681.0	220.2
	147	753.9	265.3	12.9	17.5	16.5	681.0	187.8
686 × 254	170	692.9	255.8	14.5	23.7	15.2	610.5	216.3
	152	687.6	254.5	13.2	21.0	15.2	610.5	193.6
	140	683.5	253.7	12.4	19.0	15.2	610.5	178.4
	125	677.9	253.0	11.7	16.2	15.2	610.5	159.4
914 × 419	388	920.5	420.5	21.5	36.6	24.1	799.0	494.5
	343	911.4	418.5	19.4	32.0	24.1	799.0	437.5
914 × 305	289	926.6	307.8	19.6	32.0	19.1	824.4	368.8
	253	918.5	305.5	17.3	27.9	19.1	824.4	322.8
	224	910.3	304.1	15.9	23.9	19.1	824.4	285.3
	201	903.0	303.4	15.2	20.2	19.1	824.4	256.4
838 × 292	226	850.9	293.8	16.1	26.8	17.8	761.7	288.7
	194	840.7	292.4	14.7	21.7	17.8	761.7	247.2
	176	834.9	291.6	14.0	18.8	17.8	761.7	224.1
762 × 267	197	769.6	268.0	15.6	25.4	16.5	685.8	250.8
	173	762.0	266.7	14.3	21.6	16.5	685.8	220.5
	147	753.9	265.3	12.9	17.5	16.5	685.7	188.1
686 × 254	170	692.9	255.8	14.5	23.7	15.2	615.0	216.6
	152	687.6	254.5	13.2	21.0	15.2	615.0	193.8
	140	683.5	253.7	12.4	19.0	15.2	615.0	178.6
	125	677.9	253.0	11.7	16.2	15.2	615.0	159.6
610 × 305	238	633.0	311.5	18.6	31.4	16.5	537.2	303.8
	179	617.5	307.0	14.1	23.6	16.5	537.2	227.9
	149	609.6	304.8	11.9	19.7	16.5	537.2	190.1
610 × 229	140	617.0	230.1	13.1	22.1	12.7	547.2	178.4
	125	611,9	229.0	11.9	19.6	12.7	547.2	159.6
	113	607.3	228.2	11.2	17.3	12.7	547.2	144.5
	101	602.2	227.6	10.6	14.8	12.7	547.2	129.2
533 × 210	122	544.6	211.9	12.8	21.3	12.7	476.5	155.8
	109	539.5	210.7	11.6	18.8	12.7	476.5	138.6
	101	536.7	210.1	10.9	17.4	12.7	476.5	129.3
	92	533.1	209.3	10.2	15.6	12.7	476.5	117.8
	82	528.3	208.7	9.6	13.2	12.7	476.5	104.4

Values in the shaded area relate to Universal Beams with tapered flanges.

UNIVERSAL BEAMS

DIMENSIONS AND PROPERTIES

Serial size	Moment of inertia			Radius of gyration		Elastic modulus		Ratio $\dfrac{D}{T}$
	Axis **x–x**		Axis	Axis	Axis	Axis	Axis	
	Gross	Net	y–y	x–x	y–y	x–x	y–y	
mm	cm⁴	cm⁴	cm⁴	cm	cm	cm³	cm³	
914 × 419	717325	642716	42481	38.1	9.27	15586	2021	25.2
	623866	559325	36251	37.8	9.11	13691	1733	28.5
914 × 305	503781	437962	14793	37.0	6.34	10874	961.3	29.0
	435796	379081	12512	36.8	6.23	9490	819.2	32.9
	375111	327298	10425	36.3	6.05	8241	685.6	38.1
	324715	284809	8632	35.6	5.81	7192	569.1	44.7
838 × 292	339130	315154	10661	34.3	6.08	7971	725.9	31.8
	278833	259610	8384	33.6	5.83	6633	573.6	38.7
	245412	228869	7111	33.1	5.64	5879	487.6	44.4
762 × 267	239464	221138	7699	30.9	5.54	6223	574.6	30.3
	204747	189347	6376	30.5	5.38	5374	478.1	35.3
	168535	156195	5002	30.0	5.16	4471	377.1	43.1
686 × 254	169843	156120	6225	28.0	5.36	4902	486 8	29.2
	150015	137962	5391	27.8	5.28	4364	423.7	32.7
	135972	125170	4789	27.6	5.18	3979	377.5	36.0
	117700	108590	3992	27.2	5.00	3472	315.5	41.8
914 × 419	718742	644135	45407	38.13	9.58	15616	2160	25.2
	625282	560743	39150	37.81	9.46	13722	1871	28.5
914 × 305	504594	438776	15610	36.99	6.51	10891	1014	29.0
	436610	379896	13318	36.78	6.42	9507	871.9	32.9
	375924	328112	11223	36.30	6.27	8259	738.1	38.1
	325529	285623	9427	35.63	6.06	7210	621.4	44.7
838 × 292	339747	315771	11353	34.30	6.27	7986	772.9	31.8
	279450	260228	9069	33.63	6.06	6648	620.4	38.7
	246029	229487	7792	33.13	5.90	5894	534.4	44.4
762 × 267	239894	221568	8174	30.93	5.71	6234	610.0	30.3
	205177	189778	6846	30.51	5.57	5385	513.4	35.3
	168966	156626	5468	29.97	5.39	4483	412.3	43.0
686 × 254	170147	156424	6621	28.03	5.53	4911	517.7	29.3
	150319	138266	5782	27.85	5.46	4372	454.5	32.7
	136276	125474	5179	27.62	5.38	3988	408.2	36.0
	118003	108894	4379	27.19	5.24	3481	346.1	41.9
610 × 305	207571	178026	15838	26.14	7.22	6559	1017	20.2
	151631	129960	11412	25.79	7.08	4911	743.3	26.1
	124660	106842	9300	25.61	6.99	4090	610.3	31.0
610 × 229	111844	101652	4512	25.04	5.03	3626	392.1	27.9
	98579	89634	3933	24.86	4.96	3222	343.5	31.2
	87431	79590	3439	24.60	4.88	2879	301.4	35.1
	75720	69087	2912	24.21	4.75	2515	255.9	40.7
533 × 210	76207	68609	3393	22.12	4.67	2799	320.2	25.5
	66739	60111	2937	21.94	4.60	2474	278.8	28.7
	61659	55557	2694	21.84	4.56	2298	256.5	30.8
	55353	49912	2392	21.68	4.51	2076	228.6	34.1
	47491	42934	2005	21.32	4.38	1798	192.2	40.0

Values in the shaded area relate to Universal Beams with tapered flanges.

In calculating the net moment of inertia, each flange of 300 mm or greater width is reduced by two holes, and each flange less than 300 mm wide by one hole.

Table 2.9 Section properties of universal beams

UNIVERSAL BEAMS

DIMENSIONS AND PROPERTIES

Serial size	Mass per metre	Depth of section D	Width of section B	Thickness		Root radius r	Depth between fillets d	Area of section
				Web t	Flange T			
mm	kg	mm	mm	mm	mm	mm	mm	cm²
457 × 191	98	467.4	192.8	11.4	19.6	10.2	407.9	125.3
	89	463.6	192.0	10.6	17.7	10.2	407.9	113.9
	82	460.2	191.3	9.9	16.0	10.2	407.9	104.5
	74	457.2	190.5	9.1	14.5	10.2	407.9	95.0
	67	453.6	189.9	8.5	12.7	10.2	407.9	85.4
457 × 152	82	465.1	153.5	10.7	18.9	10.2	406.9	104.5
	74	461.3	152.7	9.9	17.0	10.2	406.9	95.0
	67	457.2	151.9	9.1	15.0	10.2	406.9	85.4
	60	454.7	152.9	8.0	13.3	10.2	407.7	75.9
	52	449.8	152.4	7.6	10.9	10.2	407.7	66.5
406 × 178	74	412.8	179.7	9.7	16.0	10.2	360.5	95.0
	67	409.4	178.8	8.8	14.3	10.2	360.5	85.5
	60	406.4	177.8	7.8	12.8	10.2	360.5	76.0
	54	402.6	177.6	7.6	10.9	10.2	360.5	68.4
406 × 140	46	402.3	142.4	6.9	11.2	10.2	359.6	59.0
	39	397.3	141.8	6.3	8.6	10.2	359.6	49.4
356 × 171	67	364.0	173.2	9.1	15.7	10.2	312.2	85.4
	57	358.6	172.1	8.0	13.0	10.2	312.2	72.2
	51	355.6	171.5	7.3	11.5	10.2	312.2	64.6
	45	352.0	171.0	6.9	9.7	10.2	312.2	57.0
356 × 127	39	352.8	126.0	6.5	10.7	10.2	311.1	49.4
	33	348.5	125.4	5.9	8.5	10.2	311.1	41.8
305 × 165	54	310.9	166.8	7.7	13.7	8.9	265.6	68.4
	46	307.1	165.7	6.7	11.8	8.9	265.6	58.9
	40	303.8	165.1	6.1	10.2	8.9	265.6	51.5
305 × 127	48	310.4	125.2	8.9	14.0	8.9	264.6	60.8
	42	306.6	124.3	8.0	12.1	8.9	264.6	53.2
	37	303.8	123.5	7.2	10.7	8.9	264.6	47.5
305 × 102	33	312.7	102.4	6.6	10.8	7.6	275.8	40.8
	28	308.9	101.9	6.1	8.9	7.6	275.8	36.3
	25	304.8	101.6	5.8	6.8	7.6	275.8	31.4
254 × 146	43	259.6	147.3	7.3	12.7	7.6	218.9	55.1
	37	256.0	146.4	6.4	10.9	7.6	218.9	47.5
	31	251.5	146.1	6.1	8.6	7.6	218.9	40.0
254 × 102	28	260.4	102.1	6.4	10.0	7.6	225.0	36.2
	25	257.0	101.9	6.1	8.4	7.6	225.0	32.2
	22	254.0	101.6	5.8	6.8	7.6	225.0	28.4
203 × 133	30	206.8	133.8	6.3	9.6	7.6	172.3	38.0
	25	203.2	133.4	5.8	7.8	7.6	172.3	32.3

UNIVERSAL BEAMS

DIMENSIONS AND PROPERTIES

Serial size	Moment of inertia			Radius of gyration		Elastic modulus		Ratio $\dfrac{D}{T}$
	Axis x–x		Axis	Axis	Axis	Axis	Axis	
	Gross	Net	y–y	x–x	y–y	x–x	y–y	
mm	cm⁴	cm⁴	cm⁴	cm	cm	cm³	cm³	
457 × 191	45717	40615	2343	19.10	4.33	1956	243.0	23.9
	41021	36456	2086	18.98	4.28	1770	217.4	26.3
	37103	32996	1871	18.84	4.23	1612	195.6	28.8
	33388	29698	1671	18.75	4.19	1461	175.5	31.6
	29401	26190	1452	18.55	4.12	1296	152.9	35.7
457 × 152	36215	32074	1143	18.62	3.31	1557	149.0	24.6
	32435	28744	1012	18.48	3.26	1406	132.5	27.1
	28577	25357	878	18.29	3.21	1250	115.5	30.6
	25464	22611	794	18.31	3.23	1120	103.9	34.2
	21345	19035	645	17.92	3.11	949.0	84.6	41.3
406 × 178	27329	24062	1545	16.96	4.03	1324	172.0	25.9
	24329	21425	1365	16.87	4.00	1188	152.7	28.6
	21508	18934	1199	16.82	3.97	1058	134.8	31.8
	18626	16457	1017	16.50	3.85	925.3	114.5	37.0
406 × 140	15647	13765	539	16.29	3.02	777.8	75.7	36.0
	12452	11017	411	15.88	2.89	626.9	58.0	46.0
356 × 171	19522	17045	1362	15.12	3.99	1073	157.3	23.2
	16077	14053	1109	14.92	3.92	896.5	128.9	27.5
	14156	12384	968	14.80	3.87	796.2	112.9	30.9
	12091	10609	812	14.57	3.78	686.9	95.0	36.2
356 × 127	10087	9213	357	14.29	2.69	571.8	56.6	33.1
	8200	7511	280	14.00	2.59	470.6	44.7	41.0
305 × 165	11710	10134	1061	13.09	3.94	753.3	127.3	22.7
	9948	8609	897	13.00	3.90	647.9	108.3	26.0
	8523	7384	763	12.86	3.85	561.2	92.4	29.9
305 × 127	9504	8643	460	12.50	2.75	612.4	73.5	22.2
	8143	7409	388	12.37	2.70	531.2	62.5	25.4
	7162	6519	337	12.28	2.67	471.5	54.6	28.4
305 × 102	6487	5800	193	12.46	2.15	415.0	37.8	29.0
	5421	4862	157	12.22	2.08	351.0	30.8	34.8
	4387	3962	120	11.82	1.96	287.9	23.6	44.6
254 × 146	6558	5706	677	10.91	3.51	505.3	92.0	20.4
	5556	4834	571	10.82	3.47	434.0	78.1	23.4
	4439	3879	449	10.53	3.35	353.1	61.5	29.1
254 × 102	4008	3569	178	10.52	2.22	307.9	34.9	26.0
	3408	3046	148	10.29	2.14	265.2	29.0	30.8
	2867	2575	120	10.04	2.05	225.7	23.6	37.2
203 × 133	2887	2476	384	8.72	3.18	279.3	57.4	21.5
	2356	2027	310	8.54	3.10	231.9	46.4	26.0

In calculating the net moment of inertia, each flange
of 300 mm or greater width is reduced by two holes,
and each flange less than 300 mm wide by one hole.

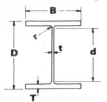

UNIVERSAL COLUMNS

DIMENSIONS AND PROPERTIES

| Serial size | Mass per metre | Depth of section D | Width of section B | Thickness | | Root radius r | Depth between fillets d | Area of section |
				Web t	Flange T			
mm	kg	mm	mm	mm	mm	mm	mm	cm²
356 × 406	634	474.7	424.1	47.6	77.0	15.2	290.1	808.1
	551	455.7	418.5	42.0	67.5	15.2	290.1	701.8
	467	436.6	412.4	35.9	58.0	15.2	290.1	595.5
	393	419.1	407.0	30.6	49.2	15.2	290.1	500.9
	340	406.4	403.0	26.5	42.9	15.2	290.1	432.7
	287	393.7	399.0	22.6	36.5	15.2	290.1	366.0
	235	381.0	395.0	18.5	30.2	15.2	290.1	299.8
Column Core	477	427.0	424.4	48.0	53.2	15.2	290.1	607.2
356 × 368	202	374.7	374.4	16.8	27.0	15.2	290.1	257.9
	177	368.3	372.1	14.5	23.8	15.2	290.1	225.7
	153	362.0	370.2	12.6	20.7	15.2	290.1	195.2
	129	355.6	368.3	10.7	17.5	15.2	290.1	164.9
305 × 305	283	365.3	321.8	26.9	44.1	15.2	246.5	360.4
	240	352.6	317.9	23.0	37.7	15.2	246.5	305.6
	198	339.9	314.1	19.2	31.4	15.2	246.5	252.3
	158	327.2	310.6	15.7	25.0	15.2	246.5	201.2
	137	320.5	308.7	13.8	21.7	15.2	246.5	174.6
	118	314.5	306.8	11.9	18.7	15.2	246.5	149.8
	97	307.8	304.8	9.9	15.4	15 2	246.5	123.3
254 × 254	167	289.1	264.5	19.2	31.7	12.7	200.2	212.4
	132	276.4	261.0	15.6	25.1	12.7	200.2	167.7
	107	266.7	258.3	13.0	20.5	12.7	200.2	136.6
	89	260.4	255.9	10.5	17.3	12.7	200.2	114.0
	73	254.0	254.0	8.6	14.2	12.7	200.2	92.9
203 × 203	86	222.3	208.8	13.0	20.5	10.2	160.8	110.1
	71	215.9	206.2	10.3	17.3	10.2	160.8	91.1
	60	209.6	205.2	9.3	14.2	10.2	160.8	75.8
	52	206.2	203.9	8.0	12.5	10.2	160.8	66.4
	46	203.2	203.2	7.3	11.0	10.2	160.8	58.8
152 × 152	37	161.8	154.4	8.1	11.5	7.6	123.4	47.4
	30	157.5	152.9	6.6	9.4	7.6	123.4	38.2
	23	152.4	152.4	6.1	6.8	7.6	123.4	29.8

UNIVERSAL COLUMNS

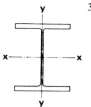

DIMENSIONS AND PROPERTIES

Serial size	Moment of inertia			Radius of gyration		Elastic modulus		Ratio
	Axis x–x		Axis y–y	Axis x–x	Axis y–y	Axis x–x	Axis y–y	$\dfrac{D}{T}$
	Gross	Net						
mm	cm⁴	cm⁴	cm⁴	cm	cm	cm³	cm³	
356 × 406	275140	243065	98211	18.5	11.0	11592	4632	6.2
	227023	200308	82665	18.0	10.9	9964	3951	6.7
	183118	161334	67905	17.5	10.7	8388	3293	7.5
	146765	129152	55410	17.1	10.5	7004	2723	8.5
	122474	107674	46816	16.8	10.4	6027	2324	9.5
	99994	87837	38714	16.5	10.3	5080	1940	10.8
	79110	69430	31008	16.2	10.2	4153	1570	12.6
Column Core	172391	152946	68056	16.8	10.6	8075	3207	8.0
356 × 368	66307	57805	23632	16.0	9.57	3540	1262	13.9
	57153	49791	20470	15.9	9.52	3104	1100	15.5
	48525	42263	17469	15.8	9.46	2681	943.8	17.5
	40246	35047	14555	15.6	9.39	2264	790.4	20.3
305 × 305	78777	66878	24545	14.8	8.25	4314	1525	8.3
	64177	54405	20239	14.5	8.14	3641	1273	9.3
	50832	43039	16230	14.2	8.02	2991	1034	10.8
	38740	32783	12524	13.9	7.89	2368	806.3	13.1
	32838	27782	10672	13.7	7.82	2049	691.4	14.8
	27601	23344	9006	13.6	7.75	1755	587.0	16.8
	22202	18776	7268	13.4	7.68	1442	476.9	20.0
254 × 254	29914	27171	9796	11.9	6.79	2070	740.6	9.1
	22416	20350	7444	11.6	6.66	1622	570.4	11.0
	17510	15889	5901	11.3	6.57	1313	456.9	13.0
	14307	12973	4849	11.2	6.52	1099	378.9	15.0
	11360	10299	3873	11.1	6.46	894.5	305.0	17.9
203 × 203	9462	8373	3119	9.27	5.32	851.5	298.7	10.8
	7647	6756	2536	9.16	5.28	708.4	246.0	12.4
	6088	5383	2041	8.96	5.19	581.1	199.0	14.8
	5263	4651	1770	8.90	5.16	510.4	173.6	16.5
	4564	4035	1539	8.81	5.11	449.2	151.5	18.5
152 × 152	2218	1931	709	6.84	3.87	274.2	91.78	14.0
	1742	1516	558	6.75	3.82	221.2	73.06	16.8
	1263	1104	403	6.51	3.68	165.7	52.95	22.3

In calculating the net moment of inertia, each flange of 300 mm or greater width is reduced by two holes, and each flange less than 300 mm wide by one hole.

Table 2.11 Section properties of joists

JOISTS

DIMENSIONS AND PROPERTIES

Serial size	Mass per metre	Depth of section D	Width of section B	Thickness		Radius		Depth between fillets d	Area of section
				Web t	Flange T	Root r_1	Toe r_2		
mm	kg	mm	mm	mm	mm	mm	mm	mm	cm²
254 × 203	*81.85*	254.0	203.2	10.2	19.9	19.6	9.7	166.6	104.4
254 × 114	*37.20*	254.0	114.3	7.6	12.8	12.4	6.1	199.2	47.4
203 × 152	*52.09*	203.2	152.4	8.9	16.5	15.5	7.6	133,2	66.4
203 × 102	25.33	203.2	101.6	5.8	10.4	9.4	3.2	161.0	32.3
178 × 102	21.54	177.8	101.6	5.3	9.0	9.4	3.2	138.2	27.4
152 × 127	*37.20*	152.4	127.0	10.4	13.2	13.5	6.6	94.3	47.5
152 × 89	*17.09*	152.4	88.9	4.9	8.3	7.9	2.4	117.7	21.8
152 × 76	*17.86*	152.4	76.2	5.8	9.6	9.4	4.6	111.9	22.8
127 × 114	*29.76*	127.0	114.3	10.2	11.5	9.9	4.8	79.4	37.3
127 × 114	*26.79*	127.0	114.3	7.4	11.4	9.9	5.0	79.5	34.1
127 × 76	*16.37*	127.0	76.2	5.6	9.6	9.4	4.6	86.5	21.0
127 × 76	13.36	127.0	76.2	4.5	7.6	7.9	2.4	94.2	17.0
114 × 114	*26.79*	114.3	114.3	9.5	10.7	14.3	2.4	60.8	34.4
102 × 102	23.07	101.6	101.6	9.5	10.3	11.1	3.2	55.1	29.4
102 × 64	9.65	101.6	63.5	4.1	6.6	6.9	2.4	73.2	12.3
102 × 44	*7.44*	101.6	44.4	4.3	6.1	6.9	3.3	74.7	9.5
89 × 89	*19.35*	88.9	88.9	9.5	9.9	11.1	3.2	44.1	24.9
76 × 76	*14.67*	76.2	80.0	8.9	8.4	9.5	3.2	38.0	19.1
76 × 76	12.65	76.2	76.2	5.1	8.4	9.4	4.6	37.9	16.3

Sections with mass shown in italics are, although frequently rolled, not in BS 4. Availability should be checked with BSC Sections Product Unit. Flanges of BS 4 joists have a 5° taper; all others taper at 8°.

JOISTS

DIMENSIONS AND PROPERTIES

Serial size	Moment of inertia			Radius of gyration		Elastic modulus		Ratio $\frac{D}{T}$
	Axis x–x		Axis y–y	Axis x–x	Axis y–y	Axis x–x	Axis y–y	
	Gross	Net						
mm	cm⁴	cm⁴	cm⁴	cm	cm	cm³	cm³	
254 × 203	12016	10527	2278	10.7	4.67	946.2	224.3	12.8
254 × 114	5092	4243	270.1	10.4	2.39	401.0	47.19	19.8
203 × 152	4789	4177	813.3	8.48	3.51	471.3	106.7	12.3
203 × 102	2294	2024	162.6	8.43	2.25	225.8	32.02	19.5
178 × 102	1519	1339	139.2	7.44	2.25	170.9	27.41	19.8
152 × 127	1818	1627	378.8	6.20	2.82	238.6	59.65	11.5
152 × 89	881.1	762.6	85.98	6.36	1.99	115.6	19.34	18.4
152 × 76	873.7	736.2	60.77	6.20	1.63	114.7	15.90	15.9
127 × 114	979.0	866.9	241.9	5.12	2.55	154.2	42.32	11.0
127 × 114	944.8	834.6	235.4	5.26	2.63	148.8	41.19	11.1
127 × 76	569.4	476.1	60.35	5.21	1.70	89.64	15.90	13.2
127 × 76	475.9	400.0	50.18	5.29	1.72	74.94	13.17	16.7
114 × 114	735.4	651.2	223.1	4.62	2.54	128.6	39.00	10.7
102 × 102	486.1	425.1	154.4	4.06	2.29	95.70	30.32	9.9
102 × 64	217.6	182.2	25.30	4.21	1.43	42.84	7.97	15.4
102 × 44	152.3	126.9	7.91	4.01	0.91	29.99	3.44	16.7
89 × 89	306.7	263.7	101.1	3.51	2.01	68.99	22.78	9.0
76 × 76	171.9	144.1	60.77	3.00	1.78	45.06	15.24	9.1
76 × 76	158.6	130.7	52.03	3.12	1.78	41.62	13.60	9.1

In calculating the net moment of inertia, one hole is deducted from each flange.

Table 2.12 Section properties of channels

CHANNELS

DIMENSIONS AND PROPERTIES

| Serial size | Mass per metre | Depth of section | Width of section | Thickness | | Radius | | Depth between fillets | Area of section | Ratio |
		D	B	Web t	Flange T	Root r_1	Toe r_2	d		$\frac{D}{T}$
mm	kg	mm	mm	mm	mm	mm	mm	mm	cm²	
432 × **102**	65.54	431.8	101.6	12.2	16.8	15.2	4.8	362.4	83.49	25.6
381 × **102**	55.10	381.0	101.6	10.4	16.3	15.2	4.8	312.4	70.19	23.3
305 × **102**	46.18	304.8	101.6	10.2	14.8	15.2	4.8	239.2	58.83	20.5
305 × **89**	41.69	304.8	88.9	10.2	13.7	13.7	3.2	245.4	53.11	22.3
254 × **89**	35.74	254.0	88.9	9.1	13.6	13.7	3.2	194.7	45.52	18.7
254 × **76**	28.29	254.0	76.2	8.1	10.9	12.2	3.2	203.8	36.03	23.2
229 × **89**	32.76	228.6	88.9	8.6	13.3	13.7	3.2	169.8	41.73	17.2
229 × **76**	26.06	228.6	76.2	7.6	11.2	12.2	3.2	178.0	33.20	20.5
203 × **89**	29.78	203.2	88.9	8.1	12.9	13.7	3.2	145.2	37.94	15.8
203 × **76**	23.82	203.2	76.2	7.1	11.2	12.2	3.2	152.5	30.34	18.2
178 × **89**	26.81	177.8	88.9	7.6	12.3	13.7	3.2	121.0	34.15	14.5
178 × **76**	20.84	177.8	76.2	6.6	10.3	12.2	3.2	128.8	26.54	17.3
152 × **89**	23.84	152.4	88.9	7.1	11.6	13.7	3.2	97.0	30.36	13.2
152 × **76**	17.88	152.4	76.2	6.4	9.0	12.2	2.4	105.9	22.77	16.9
127 × **64**	14.90	127.0	63.5	6.4	9.2	10.7	2.4	84.0	18.98	13.8
102 × **51**	10.42	101.6	50.8	6.1	7.6	9.1	2.4	65.7	13.28	13.3
76 × **38**	6.70	76.2	38.1	5.1	6.8	7.6	2.4	45.8	8.53	11.2

CHANNELS

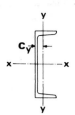

DIMENSIONS AND PROPERTIES

Serial size	Dimension Cy	Moment of inertia			Radius of gyration		Elastic modulus	
		Axis x–x		Axis y–y	Axis x–x	Axis y–y	Axis x–x	Axis y–y
		Gross	Net					
mm	cm	cm⁴	cm⁴	cm⁴	cm	cm	cm³	cm³
432 × 102	2.32	21399	17592	628.6	16.0	2.74	991.1	80.14
381 × 102	2.52	14894	12053	579.7	14.6	2.87	781.8	75.86
305 × 102	2.66	8214	6583	499.5	11.8	2.91	539.0	66.59
305 × 89	2.18	7061	5826	325.4	11.5	2.48	463.3	48.49
254 × 89	2.42	4448	3612	302.4	9.88	2.58	350.2	46.70
254 × 76	1.86	3367	2669	162.6	9.67	2.12	265.1	28.21
229 × 89	2.53	3387	2732	285.0	9.01	2.61	296.4	44.82
229 × 76	2.00	2610	2041	158.7	8.87	2.19	228.3	28.22
203 × 89	2.65	2491	1996	264.4	8.10	2.64	245.2	42.34
203 × 76	2.13	1950	1508	151.3	8.02	2.23	192.0	27.59
178 × 89	2.76	1753	1397	241.0	7.16	2.66	197.2	39.29
178 × 76	2.20	1337	1028	134.0	7.10	2.25	150.4	24.72
152 × 89	2.86	1166	924.1	215.1	6.20	2.66	153.0	35.70
152 × 76	2.21	851.5	653.6	113.8	6.12	2.24	111.8	21.05
127 × 64	1.94	482.5	367.1	67.23	5.04	1.88	75.99	15.25
102 × 51	1.51	207.7	167.8	29.10	3.95	1.48	40.89	8.16
76 × 38	1.19	74.14	54.48	10.66	2.95	1.12	19.46	4.07

In calculating the moment of inertia, each flange is reduced by one hole.

Table 2.13 Section properties of equal angles

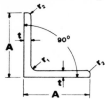

EQUAL ANGLES

DIMENSIONS AND PROPERTIES

Designation		Leg length A	Thickness t	Mass per metre	Radius		Area of section	Distance of centre of gravity c
Size	Thickness				Root r_1	Toe r_2		
mm	mm	mm	mm	kg	mm	mm	cm²	cm
200 × 200	24		24	71.1			90.6	5.84
	20		20	59.9			76.3	5.68
	18	200	18	54.2	18	4.8	69.1	5.60
	16		16	48.5			61.8	5.52
150 × 150	18		18	40.1			51.0	4.37
	15		15	33.8			43.0	4.25
	12	150	12	27.3	16	4.8	34.8	4.12
	10		10	23.0			29.3	4.03
120 × 120	15		15	26.6			33.9	3.51
	12		12	21.6			27.5	3.40
	10	120	10	18.2	13	4.8	23.2	3.31
	8		8	14.7			18.7	3.23
100 × 100	15		15	21.9			27.9	3.02
	12	100	12	17.8	12	4.8	22.7	2.90
	8		8	12.2			15.5	2.74
90 × 90	12		12	15.9			20.3	2.66
	10		10	13.4			17.1	2.58
	8	90	8	10.9	11	4.8	13.9	2.50
	6		6	8.30			10.6	2.41
80 × 80	10		10	11.9			15.1	2.34
	8	80	8	9.63	10	4.8	12.3	2.26
	6		6	7.34			9.35	2.17

Some of the thicknesses given in this table are obtained by raising the rolls. (Practice in this respect is not uniform throughout the industry.) In such cases the legs will be slightly longer and the backs of the toes will be slightly rounded.

100 × 100 × 10 mm angle is also frequently rolled; as an ISO size its properties are given in Appendix A (Table A1) to BS 4848:Part 4. Other non-standard sections, particularly other thicknesses of the standard range, may also be available.

EQUAL ANGLES

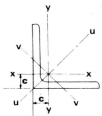

DIMENSIONS AND PROPERTIES

Moment of inertia			Radius of gyration			Elastic modulus
Axis x–x, y–y	Axis u–u	Axis v–v	Axis x–x, y–y	Axis u–u	Axis v–v	Axis x–x, y–y
cm^4	cm^4	cm^4	cm	cm	cm	cm^3
3330	5280	1380	6.06	7.64	3.90	235
2850	4530	1170	6.11	7.70	3.92	199
2600	4130	1070	6.13	7.73	3.93	181
2340	3720	959	6.16	7.76	3.94	162
1050	1670	435	4.54	5.71	2.92	98.7
898	1430	370	4.57	5.76	2.93	83.5
737	1170	303	4.60	5.80	2.95	67.7
624	991	258	4.62	5.82	2.97	56.9
445	705	185	3.62	4.56	2.33	52.4
368	584	151	3.65	4.60	2.35	42.7
313	497	129	3.67	4.63	2.36	36.0
255	405	105	3.69	4.65	2.37	29.1
249	393	104	2.98	3.75	1.93	35.6
207	328	85.7	3.02	3.80	1.94	29.1
145	230	59.8	3.06	3.85	1.96	19.9
148	234	61.7	2.70	3.40	1.75	23.3
127	201	52.6	2.72	3.42	1.76	19.8
104	166	43.1	2.74	3.45	1.76	16.1
80.3	127	33.3	2.76	3.47	1.78	12.2
87.5	139	36.3	2.41	3.03	1.55	15 4
72.2	115	29.8	2.43	3.06	1.56	12.6
55.8	88.5	23.1	2.44	3.08	1.57	9.57

Some of the thicknesses given in this table are obtained by raising the rolls. (Practice in this respect is not uniform throughout the industry.) In such cases the legs will be slightly longer and the backs of the toes will be slightly rounded.

100 × 100 × 10 mm angle is also frequently rolled; as an ISO size its properties are given in Appendix A (Table A1) to BS 4848:Part 4. Other non-standard sections, particularly other thicknesses of the standard range, may also be available.

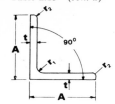

EQUAL ANGLES

DIMENSIONS AND PROPERTIES

Designation		Leg length **A**	Thickness **t**	Mass per metre	Radius		Area of section	Distance of centre of gravity **c**
Size	Thickness				Root r_1	Toe r_2		
mm	mm	mm	mm	kg	mm	mm	cm²	cm
70 × 70	10		10	10.3			13.1	2.09
	8	70	8	8.36	9	2.4	10.6	2.01
	6		6	6.38			8.13	1.93
60 × 60	10		10	8.69			11.1	1.85
	8		8	7.09			9.03	1.77
	6	60	6	5.42	8	2.4	6.91	1.69
	5		5	4.57			5.82	1.64
50 × 50	8		8	5.82			7.41	1.52
	6	50	6	4.47	7	2.4	5.59	1.45
	5		5	3.77			4.80	1.40
45 × 45	6		6	4.00			5.09	1.32
	5	45	5	3.38	7	2.4	4.30	1.28
	4		4	2.74			3.49	1.23
40 × 40	6		6	3.52			4.48	1.20
	5	40	5	2.97	6	2.4	3.79	1.16
	4		4	2.42			3.08	1.12
25 × 25	5		5	1.77			2.26	0.80
	4	25	4	1.45	3.5	2.4	1.85	0.76
	3		3	1.11			1.42	0.72

Some of the thicknesses given in this table are obtained by raising the rolls. (Practice in this respect is not uniform throughout the industry.) In such cases the legs will be slightly longer and the backs of the toes will be slightly rounded.

100 × 100 × 10 mm angle is also frequently rolled; as an ISO size its properties are given in Appendix A (Table A1) to BS 4848:Part 4. Other non-standard sections, particularly other thicknesses of the standard range, may also be available.

EQUAL ANGLES

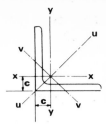

DIMENSIONS AND PROPERTIES

Moment of inertia			Radius of gyration			Elastic modulus
Axis x–x, y–y	Axis u–u	Axis v–v	Axis x–x, y–y	Axis u–u	Axis v–v	Axis x–x, y–y
cm⁴	cm⁴	cm⁴	cm	cm	cm	cm³
57.2	90.5	23.9	2.09	2.63	1.35	11.7
47.5	75.3	19.7	2.11	2.66	1.36	9.52
36.9	58.5	15.2	2.13	2.68	1.37	7.27
34.9	55.1	14.8	1.78	2.23	1.16	8.41
29.2	46.2	12.1	1.80	2.26	1.16	6.89
22.8	36.2	9.43	1.82	2.29	1.17	5.29
19.4	30.7	8.02	1.82	2.30	1.17	4.45
16.3	25.7	6.87	1.48	1.86	0.96	4.68
12.8	20.4	5.33	1.50	1.89	0.97	3.61
11.0	17.4	4.54	1.51	1.90	0.97	3.05
9.16	14.5	3.82	1.34	1.69	0.87	2.88
7.84	12.4	3.25	1.35	1.70	0.87	2.43
6.43	10.2	2.67	1.36	1.71	0.87	1.97
6.31	9.98	2.65	1.19	1.49	0.77	2.26
5.43	8.60	2.26	1.20	1.51	0.77	1.91
4.47	7.09	1.85	1.21	1.52	0.78	1.55
1.20	1.89	0.52	0.73	0.91	0.48	0.71
1.01	1.60	0.43	0.74	0.93	0.48	0.58
0.80	1.26	0.33	0.75	0.94	0.48	0.45

Some of the thicknesses given to this table are obtained by raising the rolls. (Practice in this respect is not uniform throughout the industry.) In such cases the legs will be slightly longer and the backs of the toes will be slightly rounded.

100 × 100 × 10 mm angle is also frequently rolled; as an ISO size its properties are given in Appendix A (Table A1) to BS 4848:Part 4. Other non-standard sections, particularly other thicknesses of the standard range, may also be available.

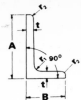

UNEQUAL ANGLES

DIMENSIONS AND PROPERTIES

Designation		Leg lengths		Thickness	Mass per metre	Radius		Area of section	Distance of centre of gravity	
Size	Thickness	A	B	t		Root r_1	Toe r_2		cx	cy
mm	mm	mm	mm	mm	kg	mm	mm	cm²	cm	cm
200 × 150	18	200	150	18	47.1	15	4.8	60.0	6.33	3.85
	15			15	39.6			50.5	6.21	3.73
	12			12	32.0			40.8	6.08	3.61
200 × 100	15	200	100	15	33.7	15	4.8	43.0	7.16	2.22
	12			12	27.3			34.8	7.03	2.10
	10			10	23.0			29.2	6.93	2.01
150 × 90	15	150	90	15	26.6	12	4.8	33.9	5.21	2.23
	12			12	21.6			27.5	5.08	2.12
	10			10	18.2			23.2	5.00	2.04
150 × 75	15	150	75	15	24.8	11	4.8	31.6	5.53	1.81
	12			12	20.2			25.7	5.41	1.69
	10			10	17.0			21.6	5.32	1.61
125 × 75	12	125	75	12	17.8	11	4.8	22.7	4.31	1.84
	10			10	15.0			19.1	4.23	1.76
	8			8	12.2			15.5	4.14	1.68
100 × 75	12	100	75	12	15.4	10	4.8	19.7	3.27	2.03
	10			10	13.0			16.6	3.19	1.95
	8			8	10.6			13.5	3.10	1.87

Some of the thicknesses given in this table are obtained by raising the rolls. (Practice in this respect is not uniform throughout the industry.) In such cases the legs will be slightly longer and the backs of the toes will be slightly rounded.

Additional non-standard sizes may be available, especially other thicknesses of the standard range and certain sizes in the old Imperial range, namely 125 × 75 × 6.5 and 137 × 102 × 9.5, 7.9 and 6.4 (purlin angles) and 100 × 75 × 6.5.

UNEQUAL ANGLES

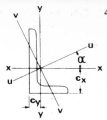

DIMENSIONS AND PROPERTIES

Moment of inertia				Radius of gyration				Elastic modulus		Angle
Axis x–x	Axis y–y	Axis u–u	Axis v–v	Axis x–x	Axis y–y	Axis u–u	Axis v–v	Axis x–x	Axis y–y	Axis x–x to Axis u–u
cm^4	cm^4	cm^4	cm^4	cm	cm	cm	cm	cm^3	cm^3	$\tan \alpha$
2376	1146	2902	618	6.29	4.37	6.95	3.21	174 0	103.0	0.548
2022	979	2475	527	6.33	4.40	7.00	3 23	147.0	86 9	0.550
1652	803	2024	431	6.36	4.44	7.04	3.25	119.0	70.5	0.552
1758	299	1863	194	6.40	2.64	6.58	2.13	137.0	38.4	0.259
1440	247	1530	159	6.43	2.67	6.63	2.14	111.0	31.3	0.262
1220	210	1290	135	6.46	2.68	6.65	2.15	93 2	26 3	0.263
761	205	841	126	4.75	2.46	4.98	1.93	77.7	30.4	0.354
627	171	694	104	4.77	2.49	5.02	1.94	63.3	24.8	0.358
533	146	591	88.3	4.80	2.51	5.05	1.95	53.3	21.0	0.360
713	120	754	78.8	4.75	1 94	4 88	1 58	75.3	21.0	0.254
589	99.9	624	64.9	4.79	1.97	4.93	1.59	61.4	17.2	0.259
501	85.8	532	55.3	4 81	1.99	4.96	1.60	51.8	14.6	0.261
354	95.5	391	58.5	3.95	2.05	4.15	1.61	43.2	16.9	0.353
302	82.1	334	50.0	3.97	2.07	4.18	1.62	36.5	14.3	0.356
247	67.6	274	40.9	4.00	2.09	4.20	1.63	29.6	11.6	0.359
189	90.2	230	49.5	3.10	2.14	3.42	1.59	28.0	16.5	0.540
162	77.6	197	42.1	3.12	2.16	3.45	1.59	23.8	14.0	0.544
133	64.1	163	34.6	3.14	2.18	3.47	1.60	19.3	11.4	0.547

Some of the thicknesses given in this table are obtained by raising the rolls. (Practice in this respect is not uniform throughout the industry.) In such cases the legs will be slightly longer and the backs of the toes will be slightly rounded.

Additional non-standard sizes may be available, especially other thicknesses of the standard range and certain sizes in the old Imperial range, namely 125 × 75 × 6.5 and 137 × 102 × 9.5, 7.9 and 6.4 (purlin angles) and 100 × 75 × 6.5.

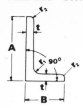

UNEQUAL ANGLES

DIMENSIONS AND PROPERTIES

Designation		Leg lengths		Thickness	Mass per metre	Radius		Area of section	Distance of centre of gravity	
Size	Thickness	A	B	t		Root r_1	Toe r_2		Cx	Cy
mm	mm	mm	mm	mm	kg	mm	mm	cm²	cm	cm
100 × 65	10			10	12.3			15.6	3.36	1.63
	8	100	65	8	9.94	10	4.8	12.7	3.27	1.55
	7			7	8.77			11.2	3.23	1.51
80 × 60	8			8	8.34			10.6	2.55	1.56
	7	80	60	7	7.36	8	4.8	9.38	2.51	1.52
	6			6	6.37			8.11	2.47	1.48
75 × 50	8	75	50	8	7.39	7	2.4	9.41	2.52	1.29
	6			6	5.65			7.19	2.44	1.21
65 × 50	8			8	6.75			8.60	2.11	1.37
	6	65	50	6	5.16	6	2.4	6.58	2.04	1.29
	5			5	4.35			5.54	1.99	1.25

Some of the thicknesses of angles given in this table are obtained by raising the rolls. (Practice in this respect is not uniform throughout the industry.) In such cases the legs will be slightly longer and the backs of the toes will be slightly rounded.

Additional non-standard sizes may be available, especially other thicknesses of the standard range and certain sizes in the old imperial range, namely 125 × 75 × 6.5 and 137 × 102 × 9.5, 7.9 and 6.4 (purlin angles) and 100 × 75 × 6.5.

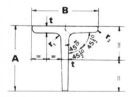

ROLLED TEES

DIMENSIONS AND PROPERTIES

Designation		Width	Depth	Thickness	Radius		Area
Size	Mass per metre	B	A	t	r_1	r_2	
mm	kg	mm	mm	mm	mm	mm	cm²
51 × 51	6.92	50.8	50.8	9.5	6.1	4.3	8.82
	4.76	50.8	50.8	6.4	6.1	4.3	6.06
44 × 44	4.11	44.4	44.4	6.4	5.8	3.8	5.24
	3.14	44.4	44.4	4.8	5.8	3.8	4.00
38 × 38	3.49	38.1	38.1	6.4	5.3	3.8	4.45
	2.66	38.1	38.1	4.8	5.3	3.8	3.39

Size 44 × 44 is a non-standard.

UNEQUAL ANGLES

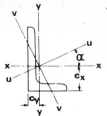

DIMENSIONS AND PROPERTIES

Moment of inertia				Radius of gyration				Elastic modulus		Angle α
Axis x–x	Axis y–y	Axis u–u	Axis v–v	Axis x–x	Axis y–y	Axis u-u	Axis v–v	Axis x–x	Axis y–y	
cm⁴	cm⁴	cm⁴	cm⁴	cm	cm	cm	cm	cm³	cm³	tan α
154	51.0	175	30.1	3.14	1.81	3.35	1.39	23.2	10.5	0.410
127	42.2	144	24.8	3.16	1.83	3.37	1.40	18.9	8.54	0.414
113	37.6	128	22.0	3.17	1.83	3.39	1.40	16.6	7.53	0.415
66.3	31.8	80.8	17.3	2.50	1.73	2.76	1.28	12.2	7.16	0.544
59.0	28.4	72.0	15.4	2.51	1.74	2.77	1.28	10.7	6.34	0.546
51.4	24.8	62.8	13.4	2.52	1.75	2.78	1.29	9.29	5.49	0.547
52.0	18.4	59.6	10.8	2.35	1.40	2.52	1.07	10.4	4.95	0.430
40.5	14.4	46.6	8.36	2.37	1.42	2.55	1.08	8.01	3.81	0.435
34.8	17.7	43.0	9.57	2.01	1.44	2.23	1.05	7.93	4.89	0.569
27.2	14.0	33.8	7.43	2.03	1.46	2.27	1.06	6.10	3.77	0.575
23.2	11.9	28.8	6.32	2.05	1.47	2.28	1.07	5.14	3.19	0.577

Some of the thicknesses of angles given in this table are obtained by raising the rolls. (Practice in this respect is not uniform throughout the industry.) In such cases the legs will be slightly longer and the backs of the toes will be slightly rounded.

Additional non-standard sizes may be available, especially other thicknesses of the standard range and certain sizes in the old imperial range, namely 125 × 75 × 6.5 and 137 × 102 × 9.5, 7.9 and 6.4 (purlin angles) and 100 × 75 × 6.5.

ROLLED TEES

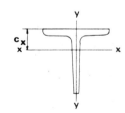

DIMENSIONS AND PROPERTIES

Centre of gravity Cx	Moment of inertia		Radius of gyration		Elastic modulus	
	Axis x–x	Axis y–y	Axis x–x	Axis y–y	Axis x–x	Axis y–y
cm	cm⁴	cm⁴	cm	cm	cm³	cm³
1.60	19.56	10.40	1.50	1.09	5.57	4.10
1.47	14.15	6.66	1.52	1.04	3.93	2.62
1.32	9.16	4.58	1.32	0.91	2.95	1.97
1.24	7.07	3.33	1.32	0.89	2.29	1.48
1.17	5.83	2.91	1.12	0.79	2.13	1.47
1.09	4.58	2.08	1.14	0.76	1.64	1.15

Size 44 × 44 is a non-standard.

3 Structural timber

3.1 DESIGN REQUIREMENTS

CP 112 Part 2: 1971, *The structural use of timber* and BS 5268 Part 2, *Permissible stress design*.

The present code of practice which deals in general with the structural use of timber (CP 112, Part 2: 1971) has now been renumbered as BS 5268, Part 2. This is in line with the policy of the British Standards Institution to replace all CP numbers with BS numbers. It is intended that BS 5268 Part 2 will form part of a new British Standard on the use of structural timber which, when complete, will have the following six parts:

Part 1, *Limit state design*.
Part 2, *Permissible stress design*.
Part 3, *Trussed rafters*.
Part 4, *Fire resistance of timber*.
Part 5, *Preservative treatments for constructional timber*.
Part 6, *Timber frame wall design*.

Part 1, *Limit state design* is in the course of preparation and its recommendations will entirely supersede those of Part 2, *Permissible stress design* after a number of years. It is not the intention of this section to give a detailed commentary on the permissible stress design method of structural timber. However, sufficient guidance is provided to enable the student to undertake the design of simple beams and struts in a manner that will satisfy the basic requirements of BS 5268 Part 2.

Stress-graded timber

Timber that is to be used for structural purpose is stress-graded in accordance with BS 4978: 1973, *Specification for timber grades for structural use*. BS 4978: 1973 states that timber can be stress-graded by a visual inspection or by the use of a stress-grading machine.

Visual stress-grading is based on the physical characteristics of the timber, e.g. the number and size of knots and the slope of the grain. The timber is categorised for the purpose of grading as being either (a) GS (General structural) or (b) SS (Special structural).

Mechanical stress-grading is based on a non-destructive test that assesses the modulus of elasticity of the timber. These stress grades are specified as (c) MGS (General structural), MSS (special structural), (e) M50 or (f) M75.

Table 3.1 Green stress* (N/mm²) and moduli of elasticity (N/mm²) for visually stress-graded softwoods

Standard name	Bending		Tension		Compression parallel to grain		Compression perpendicular to grain		Shear parallel to grain		Modulus of elasticity			
											Mean		Minimum	
	SS	GS	SS	GS	SS	GS	SS	GS	SS	GS	SS	GS	SS	GS
1. Imported														
Douglas fir–larch	7·6	5·3	5·3	3·7	7·2	5·0	1·35	1·20	0·86	0·86	11300	10200	6600	6000
Hem–fir	5·9	4·0	4·0	2·9	5·9	4·0	1·03	0·92	0·70	0·70	9500	8500	5900	5200
Parana pine	5·9	4·0	4·0	2·9	6·7	4·6	1·14	1·01	0·76	0·76	9500	8500	5400	4800
Pitch-pine	7·6	5·3	5·3	3·7	7·2	5·0	1·35	1·20	0·86	0·86	11900	10700	7800	7000
Redwood	5·9	4·0	4·0	2·9	5·4	3·7	1·14	1·01	0·70	0·70	8200	7000	4700	4000
Whitewood	5·9	4·0	4·0	2·9	5·4	3·7	1·03	0·92	0·70	0·70	8200	7000	4700	4000
Spruce–pine–fir	5·5	3·8	3·8	2·7	5·4	3·7	1·03	0·92	0·70	0·70	8000	7200	4300	3900
Western red cedar	4·5	3·2	3·2	2·2	4·0	2·8	0·77	0·69	0·62	0·62	7400	6700	5000	4600
2. Home-grown														
Douglas fir	7·3	5·1	5·1	3·6	6·7	4·6	1·29	1·15	0·70	0·70	9800	8800	4700	4200
Larch	6·9	4·8	4·8	3·4	6·3	4·4	1·35	1·20	0·86	0·86	9200	8200	4400	4000
Scots pine	5·5	3·8	3·8	2·7	5·4	3·7	1·29	1·15	0·70	0·70	9000	8100	4300	3900
European spruce	4·2*	2·9	2·9	2·0	4·0	2·8	0·82	0·73	0·55	0·55	6100	5500	3200	2900
Sitka spruce	3·8	2·7	2·7	1·9	3·6	2·5	0·82	0·73	0·55	0·55	6500	5900	3100	2800

* These stresses apply to timber having a moisture content exceeding 18%.

Table 3.2 Green stresses* (N/mm²) and moduli of elasticity (N/mm²) for machine stress-graded softwoods

Property	Grade	Standard name					
		Western hemlock (commercial)	Redwood and whitewood	Douglas fir (home-grown)	Scots pine (home-grown)	Sitka spruce (home-grown)	Western white spruce
Bending	M75	8·1	8·1	10·0	7·0	4·9	7·6
	M50	5·3	5·3	6·7	4·5	3·3	5·0
	MSS	5·9	5·9	7·3	5·5	3·8	5·5
	MGS	4·0	4·0	5·1	3·8	2·7	3·8
Tension	M75	5·7	5·7	7·0	4·8	3·4	5·3
	M50	3·7	3·7	4·7	3·1	2·3	3·5
	MSS	4·0	4·0	5·1	3·8	2·7	3·8
	MGS	2·9	2·9	3·6	2·7	1·9	2·7
Compression parallel to grain	M75	7·9	7·3	9·2	6·7	4·6	7·3
	M50	5·2	4·8	6·1	4·3	3·1	4·8
	MSS	5·9	5·4	6·7	5·4	3·6	5·4
	MGS	4·0	3·7	4·6	3·7	2·5	3·7
Compression perpendicular to grain	M75	1·20	1·20**	1·50	1·50	0·97	1·20
	M50	1·03	1·03**	1·29	1·29	0·82	1·03
	MSS	1·03	1·03**	1·29	1·29	0·82	1·03
	MGS	0·92	0·92**	1·15	1·15	0·73	0·92
Shear parallel to grain	M75	1·03	1·03	1·03	1·03	0·82	1·03
	M50	0·70	0·70	0·70	0·70	0·55	0·70
	MSS	0·70	0·70	0·70	0·70	0·55	0·70
	MGS	0·70	0·70	0·70	0·70	0·55	0·70
Mean modulus of elasticity	M75	10600	8700	11300	10300	7500	9200
	M50	9300	7300	9500	9000	6400	7700
	MSS	9600	8300	9700	9600	6800	8300
	MGS	8700	7200	8600	8700	6000	7400
Minimum modulus of elasticity	M75	7100	5500	7100	6800	4600	5800
	M50	6200	4500	6200	6000	4000	4900
	MSS	6400	5200	6400	6400	4200	5200
	MGS	5800	4400	5800	5800	3700	4600

* These stresses apply to timber having a moisture content exceeding 18%.
** Where redwood is used separately these stresses may be increased by a factor of 1·1.

Table 3.3 Dry stresses* (N/mm²) and moduli of elasticity (N/mm²) for visually stress-graded softwoods

Standard name	Bending		Tension		Compression parallel to grain		Compression perpendicular to grain		Shear parallel to grain		Modulus of elasticity			
											Mean		Minimum	
	SS	GS	SS	GS	SS	GS	SS	GS	SS	GS	SS	GS	SS	GS
1. Imported														
Douglas fir–larch	9·3	6·5	6·5	4·6	9·6	6·7	2·00	1·80	0·96	0·96	12500	11300	7300	6600
Hem-fir	7·3	5·1	5·1	3·5	7·9	5·5	1·55	1·38	0·80	0·80	10700	9600	6600	5900
Parana pine	7·3	5·1	5·1	3·5	9·1	6·3	1·71	1·52	0·90	0·90	10500	9400	6000	5300
Pitch-pine	9·3	6·5	6·5	4·6	9·1	6·3	2·00	1·80	0·94	0·94	12900	11600	8500	7600
Redwood	7·3	5·1	5·1	3·5	8·0	5·6	1·71	1·52	0·86	0·86	10000	8600	5700	4900
Whitewood	7·3	5·1	5·1	3·5	8·0	5·6	1·55	1·38	0·86	0·86	10000	8600	5700	4900
Spruce–pine–fir	6·9	4·8	4·8	3·3	7·0	4·8	1·55	1·38	0·79	0·79	8900	8000	4800	4300
Western red cedar	5·2	3·6	3·6	2·5	5·9	4·1	1·16	1·03	0·70	0·70	8000	7200	5500	4900
2. Home-grown														
Douglas fir	9·0	6·3	6·3	4·4	9·0	6·3	1·93	1·72	0·87	0·87	10700	9800	5200	4700
Larch	8·6	6·0	6·0	4·2	8·6	6·0	2·00	1·80	1·00	1·00	10600	9500	5100	4600
Scots pine	7·6	5·3	5·3	3·7	8·0	5·6	1·93	1·72	0·86	0·86	10600	9500	5100	4600
European spruce	5·5	3·9	3·9	2·7	5·6	3·9	1·24	1·10	0·71	0·71	7500	6800	4000	3600
Sitka spruce	5·2	3·6	3·6	2·5	5·0	3·5	1·24	1·10	0·66	0·66	7800	7000	3700	3300

* These stresses apply to timber having a moisture content not exceeding 18%.

Grade stresses

The basic stresses for stress-graded timber by species are given in tables 3.1–3.4. For species groups (see below) Table 3.5 and 3.6 should be consulted. Table 3.1, 3.2 and 3.5 are for 'green timber', i.e. timber with a moisture content greater than 18%. Tables 3.3, 3.4 and 3.6 are for 'dry timber', i.e. timber with a moisture content of less than 18%.

Species groups

Table 3.7 lists the softwoods most commonly used

Table 3.4   Dry stresses* (N/mm²) and moduli of elasticity (N/mm²) for machine stress-graded softwoods

Property	Grade	Standard name					
		Western hemlock (commercial)	Redwood and whitewood	Douglas fir (home-grown)	Scots pine (home-grown)	Sitka spruce (home-grown)	Western white spruce
Bending	M75	10·0	10·0	12·4	9·6	6·6	9·7
	M50	6·6	6·6	8·3	6·2	4·5	6·2
	MSS	7·3	7·3	9·0	7·6	5·2	6·9
	MGS	5·1	5·1	6·3	5·3	3·6	4·8
Tension	M75	7·0	7·0	8·7	6·7	4·6	6·7
	M50	4·6	4·6	5·8	4·3	3·2	4·3
	MSS	5·1	5·1	6·3	5·3	3·6	4·8
	MGS	3·5	3·5	4·4	3·7	2·5	3·3
Compression parallel to grain	M75	10·8	10·8	12·4	10·0	6·4	9·5
	M50	7·1	7·1	8·3	6·5	4·3	6·3
	MSS	7·9	8·0	9·0	8·0	5·0	7·0
	MGS	5·5	5·6	6·3	5·6	3·5	4·8
Compression perpendicular to grain	M75	1·80	1·80**	2·25	2·25	1·45	1·80
	M50	1·55	1·55**	1·93	1·93	1·24	1·55
	MSS	1·55	1·55**	1·93	1·93	1·24	1·55
	MGS	1·38	1·38**	1·72	1·72	1·10	1·38
Shear parallel to grain	M75	1·19	1·28	1·30	1·28	0·98	1·19
	M50	0·80	0·86	0·87	0·86	0·66	0·79
	MSS	0·80	0·86	0·87	0·86	0·66	0·79
	MGS	0·80	0·86	0·87	0·86	0·66	0·79
Mean modulus of elasticity	M75	12 000	10 700	12 500	12 000	9 000	10 200
	M50	10 500	9 000	10 500	10 500	7 700	8 600
	MSS	10 800	10 200	10 800	11 200	8 200	9 200
	MGS	9 800	8 800	9 500	10 200	7 200	8 200
Minimum modulus of elasticity	M75	8 000	6 700	8 000	8 000	5 500	6 400
	M50	7 000	5 500	7 000	7 000	4 800	5 400
	MSS	7 200	6 400	7 200	7 500	5 100	5 800
	MGS	6 500	5 400	6 500	6 800	4 500	5 100

* These stresses apply to timber having a moisture content not exceeding 18%.
** Where redwood is used separately these stresses may be increased by a factor of 1·1.

Table 3.5   Green stresses* (N/mm²) and moduli of elasticity (N/mm²) for grouped softwoods

Species group**	Grade	Bending	Tension	Compression parallel to grain	Compression perpendicular to grain	Shear parallel to grain	Modulus of elasticity	
							Mean	Minimum
S1	SS	6·9	4·8	6·3	1·29	0·70	9200	4400
	GS	4·8	3·4	4·4	1·15	0·70	8200	4000
S2	SS	5·5	3·8	5·4	1·03	0·70	8000	4300
	GS	3·8	2·7	3·7	0·92	0·70	700	3900
S3	SS	3·8	2·7	3·6	0·77	0·55	6100	3100
	GS	2·7	1·9	2·5	0·69	0·55	5500	2800

* These stresses apply to timber having a moisture content exceeding 18%.
** The species groups are defined in Table 3.7.

Table 3.6 Dry stresses* (N/mm²) and moduli of elasticity (N/mm²) for grouped softwoods

Species group**	Grade	Bending	Tension	Compression parallel to grain	Compression perpendicular to grain	Shear parallel to grain	Modulus of elasticity	
							Mean	Minimum
S1	SS	8·6	6·0	8·6	1·93	0·87	10 600	5 100
	GS	6·0	4·2	6·0	1·72	0·87	9 500	4 600
S2	SS	6·9	4·8	7·0	1·55	0·79	8 900	4 800
	GS	4·8	3·3	4·8	1·38	0·79	8 000	4 300
S3	SS	5·2	3·6	5·0	1·16	0·66	7 500	3 700
	GS	3·6	2·5	3·5	1·03	0·66	6 800	3 300

* These stresses apply to timber having a moisture content not exceeding 18%.
** The species groups are defined in Table 3.7.

Table 3.7 Softwood species groups

Species group	Name of Timber
S1	Douglas fir, Douglas fir–larch, pitch-pine, larch
S2	Western hemlock, Parana pine, redwood, whitewood, Canadian spruce, Scots pine, hem-fir, princess spruce, western white spruce
S3	European spruce, Sitka spruce, western red cedar

for structural purposes in groups based on similarity in strength and stiffness. The basic grade stresses given in Table 3.5 and 3.6 are based on the weakest species of each group. Because of their wide variety and varying characteristics, hardwoods are not grouped by species.

Permissible stresses

Permissible stresses in timber are governed by the particular conditions of service and loading. They should be taken as the product of the grade stress (Tables 3.1–3.6) and the appropriate modification factor (Tables 3.8 and 3.9).

Table 3.8 Modification of stresses in flexural members for duration of loading

Duration of loading	Factor
Long term (e.g. dead + permanent imposed)	1·00
Medium term (e.g. dead + snow, dead + temporary)	1·25
Short term (e.g. dead + imposed + snow + wind)	1·50

Table 3.9 Modification factors for stresses in compression members of grades GS, SS, MGS, MSS and M50 softwoods

Slenderness ratio		Modification factors		
l/r	l/b	Long-term loads	Medium-term loads	Short-term loads
<5	1·4	1·00	1·25	1·50
5	1·4	0·99	1·24	1·49
10	2·9	0·98	1·23	1·47
20	5·8	0·96	1·20	1·44
30	8·7	0·94	1·17	1·40
40	11·5	0·91	1·13	1·34
50	14·4	0·87	1·08	1·27
60	17·3	0·83	1·00	1·16
70	20·2	0·77	0·90	1·01
80	23·0	0·70	0·79	0·86
90	26·0	0·61	0·68	0·72
100	28·8	0·53	0·58	0·60
120	34·6	0·40	0·42	0·44
140	40·4	0·31	0·32	0·33
160	46·2	0·24	0·25	0·25
180*	52·0	0·20	0·20	0·20
200	57·7	0·16	0·16	0·17
220	63·5	0·13	0·14	0·14
240	69·2	0·11	0·12	0·12
250	72·2	0·10	0·11	0·11

* Limiting value for compression members carrying dead and superimposed loading.

Modification factors

Duration of loading

For medium- and short-term loading, permissible stresses can be increased by the factors shown in Table 3.8. No increase is allowed for long-term loading.

Slenderness of compression members

The permissible stresses in posts and struts depend on the slenderness ratio l/r where l = the effective height or length (see Table 1.4) and r = the least radius of gyration.

For rectangular members the ratio l/b may be used, where b = the least lateral dimension.

Table 3.9 gives the modification factors for slenderness ratio and duration of loading on compresion members formed from GS, SS, MGS, MSS and M50 grades of softwood. BS 5268 Part 2 provides formulae for calculating the modification factor for M75 grade softwood and all grades of hardwood.

The maximum slenderness ratio l/r is 180 for a member carrying dead and superimposed loads, and 250 for a member carrying wind loads only.

Effective span
The span of flexural members is the distance between the centres of bearing.

Deflection
The deflection of timber floor joists when fully loaded should not exceed 0·003 of the span.

Load sharing
If four or more rafters, joists or trusses are spaced at 600 mm or closer and the load is distributed by purlins, boarding etc., grade stresses should be multiplied by 1·1.

Lateral support
Table 3.10 gives maximum depth-to-breadth ratios for various degrees of lateral support.

Compression members subject to bending
In such a member $f_{a\,par}/f_{p\,par} + C_{a\,par}/C_{p\,par}$

should not exceed 1·0 if the slenderness ration l/r is less than 20, and should not exceed 0·9 if the slenderness ratio exceeds 20, where

$f_{a\,par}$ = applied flexural stress parallel to the grain.
$f_{p\,par}$ = permissible flexural stress parallel to the grain.
$C_{a\,par}$ = applied compressive stress parallel to the grain.
$C_{p\,par}$ = permissible compressive stress parallel to the grain.

3.2 DESIGN OF BEAMS AND STRUTS

Beams of solid rectangular cross section
1. Calculate the maximum bending moment M in N mm.
2. $M = f_{p\,par}Z$, where $f_{p\,par}$ = the grade stress times the modification factor for duration of loading for bending parallel to the grain (Table 3.8), and $Z = bd^2/6$.

Therefore $M = f_{p\,par}\,bd^2/6$
hence $\quad d^2 = 6M/bf_{p\,par}$
and $\quad\quad d\sqrt{(6M/bf_{p\,par})}$

3. A suitable dimension is chosen for b from the range of standard sections available and d is then calculated. The nearest standard section with a depth greater than the calculated design depth is then chosen from Table 3.11.
4. The dimensions of the beam are then checked for deflection by calculation, using the minimum modulus of elasticity for the particular species or group. The depth-to-breadth ratio should be

Table 3.10   Maximum depth-to-breadth ratios for various degrees of lateral support

Degree of lateral support	Maximum depth-to-breadth ratio
None	2
Ends held	3
Ends held and member held in line by purlins etc.	4
Ends held and compression edge held in line by joists etc.	5
Ends held, compression edge held in line by joists etc., and bridging at spacing not greater than 6 depths	6
Ends and both edges firmly held	7

Table 3.11   Sawn softwood sizes

mm	75	100	125	150	175	200	225	250	300
16	x	x	x	x					
19	x	x	x	x					
22	x	x	x	x					
25	x	x	x	x	x	x	x	x	x
32	x	x	x	x	x	x	x	x	
38	x	x	x	x	x	x	x		
44	x	x	x	x	x	x	x	x	
50	x	x	x	x	x	x	x	x	
63		x	x	x	x	x	x		
75		x	x	x	x	x	x	x	x
100		x		x		x		x	x
150				x		x		x	x
200						x			
250								x	
300									x

checked depending on the lateral support (Table 3.10).

Strut of rectangular section carrying an axial load

1. Calculate the load W in newtons.
2. Choose a trial section.
3. Calculate the slenderness ratio l/b and determine the appropriate modification factor from Table 3.9.

Table 3.12 Typical loadings

Member	Dead load (kg/m^2)	Imposed load (kN/m^2)
Floor joists	–	1·5
Floor boards 25 mm	12·25	–
9·5 mm gypsum plaster-board (solid core)	8·3	–
Ceiling joists	–	0·75
Ceiling including thermal insulation	19·4	–
Rafters and purlins for pitched roofs covered with tiles or slates	–	See CP 3 Chapter V
Clay plain tiles (102 mm gauge)	63·5	–
Concrete plain tiles (102 mm gauge)	68·4	–
Welsh slating, 75 mm lap	48·8	–
Interlocking tiles, single lap	39·1 ± 4·9	–
Felt under tiles or slates	3·6	–
Thermal insulation, 25 mm thick	36·6	–
Purlins supporting sheeting for roofs having a pitch of $22\frac{1}{2}°$ or more	–	See CP 3 Chapter V
Asbestos cement corrugated sheeting	16·6	–

This table applies to the more commonly used timber sections. For all other sections reference should be made to BS 5268 Part 2.
4. Calculate the appropriate stress (permissible compressive stress × modification factor).
5. Multiply the cross-sectional area by the appropriate stress and compare with the load W. By a process of trial and error a suitable section is obtained.

3.3 TIMBER SIZES FOR SMALL BUILDINGS

Tables 3.13–3.17 give suitable sizes for timber members in domestic-type buildings, based on the information in Table 3.12.

Table 3.13 Minimum sizes for various flooring and roofing members

Wall plates	50 × 75
Herringbone strutting	25 × 50
Solid bridging	22, 25 and 50 thick
Ridges	25 × 125
Hips	25 × 175
Valleys	32 thick
Fascia boards	19 × 125

Slating and tiling battens … plain tiling:
  20 × 25 mm battens for rafters up to 460 mm centres
  30 × 25 mm battens for rafters over 460 mm and up to 610 mm centres

Slating and interlocking (single-lap) tiling:
  20 × 40 mm battens for rafters up to 460 mm centres
  25 × 40 mm up to 610 mm centres

Snow boarding for valley gutter:
  four lines of 25 × 50 mm or 38 × 50 mm battens on 25 × 75 mm bearers up to 760 mm centres

Table 3.14 Maximum span of ceiling joists (m)

Basic size of joist (mm)	Dead load in kg/m² supported by the joists excluding the weight of the joists															
	≤50				51–75				76–100				101–125			
	Spacing of joists in mm for centres up to															
	400	450	525	600	400	450	525	600	400	450	525	600	400	450	525	600
38 × 75	1·730	1·650	1·570	1·520	1·600	1·550	1·470	1·400	1·520	1·450	1·350	1·270	1·450	1·350	1·240	1·170
100	2·310	2·240	2·130	2·030	2·160	2·080	1·980	1·850	2·030	1·960	1·830	1·700	1·930	1·830	1·700	1·570
125	2·900	2·790	2·670	2·570	2·720	2·620	2·490	2·340	2·570	2·460	2·290	2·130	2·410	2·290	2·130	1·980
150	3·430	3·300	3·150	3·000	3·180	3·070	2·920	2·740	3·000	2·900	2·690	2·510	2·840	2·690	2·490	2·340
50 × 75	1·880	1·800	1·730	1·650	1·750	1·680	1·600	1·520	1·650	1·600	1·500	1·450	1·570	1·500	1·420	1·350
100	2·510	2·440	2·310	2·210	2·360	2·260	2·160	2·060	2·210	2·130	2·030	1·960	2·110	2·030	1·930	1·800
125	3·150	3·050	2·900	2·790	2·950	2·840	2·690	2·590	2·790	2·670	2·540	2·440	2·640	2·540	2·410	2·260
150	3·170	3·580	3·400	3·280	3·450	3·330	3·180	3·050	3·280	3·150	3·000	2·870	3·120	3·000	2·840	2·670
63 × 150	3·990	3·860	3·680	3·530	3·730	3·610	3·430	3·280	3·530	3·400	3·230	3·100	3·350	3·230	3·070	2·950
175	4·650	4·500	4·290	4·110	4·370	4·190	4·010	3·840	4·110	3·960	3·780	3·630	3·940	3·780	3·610	3·450
200	5·310	5·130	4·900	4·720	4·980	4·800	4·600	4·390	4·720	4·550	4·340	4·170	4·500	4·340	4·140	3·960
225	5·970	5·770	5·510	5·310	5·590	5·410	5·160	4·950	5·310	5·110	4·880	4·670	5·050	4·880	4·650	4·470

Table 3.15 Maximum span of floor joists (m)

Basic size of joist (mm)	Dead load in kg/m² supported by the joists excluding the weight of the joists															
	≤50				51–75				76–100				101–125			
	Spacing of joists in mm for centres up to															
	400	450	525	600	400	450	525	600	400	450	525	600	400	450	525	600
33 × 75	0·940	0·838	0·737	0·635	0·889	0·813	0·686	0·610	0·838	0·760	0·660	0·584	0·813	0·737	0·635	0·533
100	1·630	1·450	1·270	1·120	1·500	1·350	1·190	1·070	1·400	1·270	1·120	1·020	1·320	1·220	1·070	0·965
125	2·410	2·180	1·900	1·700	2·180	1·980	1·750	1·570	2·018	1·830	1·630	1·470	1·880	1·730	1·520	1·400
150	2·840	2·690	2·490	2·260	2·670	2·510	2·290	2·060	2·510	2·360	2·110	1·900	2·390	2·180	1·960	1·780
50 × 75	1·190	1·070	0·940	0·813	1·120	1·020	0·889	0·787	1·070	0·965	0·838	0·762	1·020	0·914	0·813	0·737
100	2·010	1·830	1·600	1·420	1·850	1·700	1·500	1·320	1·730	1·570	1·400	1·240	1·630	1·470	1·320	1·190
125	2·640	2·540	2·390	2·130	2·540	2·440	2·160	1·960	2·440	2·240	2·010	1·800	2·260	2·080	1·880	1·700
150	3·120	3·000	2·840	2·670	3·000	2·670	2·670	2·490	2·870	2·720	2·510	2·310	2·720	2·570	2·360	2·160
175	3·660	3·510	3·330	3·120	3·510	3·350	3·120	2·920	3·350	3·180	2·950	2·770	3·200	3·020	2·790	2·620
200	4·170	4·040	3·810	3·560	4·010	3·840	3·560	3·350	3·840	3·630	3·380	3·150	3·660	3·450	3·200	3·000
63 × 150	3·350	3·230	3·070	2·950	3·230	3·100	2·950	2·790	3·100	3·000	2·820	2·640	3·000	2·900	2·670	2·510
175	3·940	3·780	3·610	3·450	3·760	3·630	3·450	3·280	3·630	3·510	3·300	3·100	3·510	3·380	3·120	2·950
200	4·500	4·340	4·140	3·960	4·320	4·170	3·960	3·760	4·170	4·010	3·780	3·530	4·010	3·860	3·580	3·380
225	5·050	4·880	4·650	4·470	4·850	4·670	4·470	4·220	4·670	4·520	4·240	3·990	4·520	4·340	4·040	3·780

Table 3.16 Maximum span of common or jack rafters for roof pitch of over 35° but less than 40°

Basic size of rafter (mm)	Dead load in kg/m² supported by rafters excluding the dead weight of the rafters											
	≤50				51–75				76–100			
	Spacing of rafter in mm for centres up to											
	400	450	525	600	400	450	525	600	400	450	525	600
38 × 75	2·160	2·060	1·930	1·800	1·900	1·830	1·750	1·630	1·730	1·680	1·600	1·500
100	2·900	2·770	2·590	2·410	2·570	2·460	2·340	2·180	2·340	2·240	2·130	2·010
125	3·630	3·480	3·230	3·050	3·200	3·070	2·920	2·740	2·920	2·820	2·690	2·540
50 × 75	2·360	2·260	2·160	2·060	2·080	2·010	1·900	1·830	1·880	1·830	1·730	1·650
100	3·150	3·020	2·900	2·740	2·770	2·678	2·540	2·440	2·540	2·440	2·340	2·240
125	3·910	3·780	3·610	3·450	3·480	3·350	3·200	3·070	3·180	3·070	2·920	2·790

Table 3.17 Maximum span of purlins supporting rafters to which Table 3.16 relates, for roofs having a pitch of over 35° but less than 40°

Basic size of purlin (mm)	Dead load in kg/m² supported by rafters calculated from Table 3.16														
	≤50					51–75					76–100				
	Spacing of purlins in metres														
	1·83	2·13	2·44	2·74	3·05	1·83	2·13	2·44	2·74	3·05	1·83	2·13	2·44	2·74	3·05
50 × 100	1·400	1·300	1·220	1·140	1·090	1·270	1·190	1·120	1·040	0·990	1·170	1·090	1·020	0·940	0·860
125	1·780	1·630	1·520	1·450	1·370	1·570	1·500	1·400	1·320	1·240	1·450	1·370	1·300	1·190	1·070
150	2·080	1·930	1·800	1·700	1·630	1·880	1·750	1·650	1·550	1·470	1·700	1·630	1·520	1·400	1·270
175	2·440	2·260	2·110	2·010	1·900	2·180	2·060	1·930	1·830	1·730	2·010	1·900	1·780	1·650	1·470
63 × 150	2·260	2·160	2·030	1·900	1·830	2·010	1·930	1·830	1·750	1·650	1·850	1·750	1·680	1·600	1·520
175	2·670	2·540	2·390	2·240	2·130	2·360	2·260	2·160	2·030	1·930	2·160	2·060	1·980	1·880	1·800
200	3·050	2·900	2·720	2·570	2·440	2·720	2·590	2·460	2·340	2·240	2·490	2·360	2·260	2·160	2·060
75 × 175	2·280	2·690	2·590	2·460	2·340	2·510	2·390	2·290	2·210	2·130	2·310	2·210	2·110	2·030	1·960
200	3·230	3·070	2·950	2·820	2·690	2·900	2·740	2·640	2·540	2·440	2·640	2·510	2·410	2·310	2·240
225	3·630	3·480	3·330	3·200	3·020	3·250	3·100	2·970	2·840	2·770	3·000	2·840	2·720	2·620	2·540

4 Reinforced concrete

4.1 DESIGN REQUIREMENTS FROM CP 110: 1972, 'THE STRUCTURAL USE OF CONCRETE'

Many of the requirements of CP 110: 1972 are too complicated to be summarised in a book of this description. Apart from the design of the more simple elements reference should be made to the code itself.

Symbols

A_c area of concrete
A'_s area of compression reinforcement
A_{s1} area of compression in the more highly compressed face
A_s area of tension reinforcement
A_{s2} area of reinforcement in other face
A_{sc} area of longitudinal reinforcement (for columns)
A_{sv} cross-sectional area of the two legs of a link
a_b distance between bars
b width of section
b_c breadth of compression face midway between restraints
b_t breadth of section at level of tension reinforcement
b_w breadth of web or rib of a member
d effective depth of tension reinforcement
d' depth of compression reinforcement
d_2 depth to reinforcement
E_s modulus of elasticity of steel
e eccentricity
F ultimate load
F_k characteristic load
f_{bs} bond stress
f_{cu} characteristic concrete cube strength
f_k characteristic strength
f_s service stress
f_y characteristic strength of reinforcement
f_{yv} characteristic strength of link reinforcement
G_k characteristic dead load
g_k characteristic dead load per unit area or length
h overall depth of section in plane of bending
h_f thickness of flange
k a constant (with appropriate subscripts)
l distance from face of support at end of a

cantilever or effective span of a simply supported beam or slab
l_e effective height of a column or wall
l_{ex} effective height for bending about the major axis
l_{ey} effective height for bending about the minor axis
l_0 clear height of column between end restraints
l_x length of shorter side of a rectangular slab
l_y length of longer side of a rectangular slab
M bending moment due to ultimate loads
M_i maximum initial moment in a column due to ultimate loads (but not less than $0.05\,\mathrm{N\,m}$)
M_u ultimate resistance moment
N ultimate axial load at section considered
N_{bal} axial load of a column corresponding to the balanced condition
N_{uz} axial load capacity of a column ignoring all bending
n total ultimate load per unit area ($1.4g_k + 1.6q_k$)
Q_k characteristic imposed load
q_k characteristic dead load per unit area or length
r internal radius of bend
s_b spacing of bars
s_v spacing of links along the member
V shear force due to ultimate loads
v shear stress
v_c ultimate shear stress in concrete
x neutral axis depth
z lever arm
γ_f partial safety factor for load
γ_m partial safety factor for strength
ΣA_{sv} area of shear reinforcement
Σu_s sum of the effective perimeters of the tension reinforcement
φ bar size

Not all symbols associated with structural concrete are listed above. For a complete list reference should be made to CP 110 Part 1: 1972.

Limit state

CP 110 Part 1: 1972 defines limit state design as the achievement of acceptable probabilities that the structure being designed will not become unfit for

Table 4.1 Characteristic strength of concrete

Grade	f_{cu} at 28 days (N/mm^2)	Cube strength (N/mm^2) at age of:				
		7 days	*2 months*	*3 months*	*6 months*	*1 year*
20	20·0	13·5	22	23	24	25
25	25·0	16·5	27·5	29	30	31
30	30·0	20	33	35	36	37
40	40·0	28	44	45·5	47·5	50
50	50·0	36	54	55·5	57·5	60

Design may be based on f_{cu} or, if appropriate, the strength given for the age of loading.

the use for which it is required, i.e. that it will not reach a limit state. No attempt has been made in this book to derive the standard formulae used. The explanation of concepts inherent in limit state design can be found in many publications dealing with reinforced concrete design.

Characteristic loads
Since it is not yet possible to express loads in statistical terms, the following characteristic loads should be used in design.

(a) Dead loads G_k. The weight of the structure complete with finishes, partitions etc.
(b) Imposed loads Q_k. Weight due to furniture, occupants etc.
(c) Wind loads W_k.

The following publications should be used to compute the loads on the structure.

BS 648: 1964, *Schedule of weights of building materials.*
CP 3 Chapter V Part 1: 1967, *Dead loads and imposed loads.*
CP 3 Chapter V Part 2: 1972, *Wind loads.*

Characteristic strength
This term is defined by CP 110 Part 1: 1972, as that value of the cube strength of concrete or the yield or proof stress of reinforcement below which not

Table 4.2 Characteristic strength of reinforcement

Designation	Nominal sizes (mm)	$f_y (N/mm^2)$
Hot-rolled mild steel (BS 4449)	All sizes	250
Hot-rolled high yield (BS 4449)	All sizes	410
Cold-worked high yield (BS 4461)	$\leqslant 16$	460
	> 16	425
Hard-drawn steel wire (BS 4482)	$\leqslant 12$	485

Design may be based on f_y or on a lower value if necessary to reduce deflection or to control cracking.

more than 5% of the test results fail. The characteristic strength is usually represented by the 28-day cube strength of the concrete and the yield or 0·2% proof stress of the reinforcement. Typical values of characteristic strength are given in Tables 4.1 and 4.2.

Partial safety factors
1. Loads: in this case partial safety factors are introduced to take account of unforeseen variations in the characteristic loads. The partial safety factors differ for dead, imposed and wind loads and are set out in Table 4.3.
2. Materials: such partial safety factors are introduced to allow for possible differences between the characteristic strength and the actual structural

Table 4.3 Ultimate limit states

Limited states and load combination	Maximum	Minimum*	Steel**	Concrete CP 110 simplified
Collapse				
1. Dead and imposed	$1·4Gk + 1·6Qk$	$1·0Gk$	$0·87f_y$	$0·4f_{cu}$
2. Dead and wind	$1·4Gk + 1·4Wk$	$0·9Gk + 1·4Wk$	$0·87f_y$	$0·4f_{cu}$
3. Dead, imposed and wind	$1·2(Gk + Qk + Wk)$	–	$0·87f_y$	$0·4f_{cu}$
Deflection				
1. Dead and imposed	$1·0(Gk + Qk)$	$1·0Gk$	$1·0f_y$	$0·67f_{cu}$
1. Dead and wind	$1·0(Gk + Wk)$	$1·0(Gk + Wk)$	$1·0f_y$	$0·67f_{cu}$
3. Dead, imposed and wind	$1·0Gk+0·8(Qk+Wk)$	–	$1·0f_y$	$0·67f_{cu}$
local damage	As deflection	As deflection	$1·0f_y$	$0·5f_{cu}$

* The minimum applies when a reduction in load provides a more adverse condition, e.g. alternate spans in continuous systems for cases 1 and 2.
** These results are for steel in tension. For steel in compression the corresponding results are $0·72f$, for beams and $0·60f$, or $0·67f$, for columns.

strength. The values of these factors is generally taken as 1·5 for concrete and 1·15 for reinforcement.

Design loads

The design load can be defined as the characteristic load times the partial safety factor. As previously mentioned, the partial safety factors vary according to the circumstances under which the loads are considered. Maximum and minimum design loads can be obtained by reference to Table 4.3.

Effective span of beam

The effective span of a simply supported member should be taken as the smaller of

1. the distance between the centres of bearings, or
2. the clear distance between supports plus the effective depth.

Slender beams

The clear distance between lateral restraints for a simply supported beam should not exceed $60b_c$ or $250b_c{}^2/d$, whichever is the lesser.

For a cantilever beam with lateral restraint provided only at the support the clear distance from the end of the cantilever to the face of the support should not exceed $25b_c$ or $100\,b_c{}^2/d$, whichever is the lesser.

Shear resistance of beams

1. Shear stress $v = V/bd$.

2. If v is greater than v_c the whole of the shearing force should be provided for by shear reinforcement. In all cases v should not exceed the values given in Table 4.4. Values of v_c for various concrete grades and areas of tensile reinforcement are given in Table 4.5.

Table 4.4   Maximum value of shear stress (N/mm^2) in beams for various concrete grades

Concrete grade			
20	25	30	40 or more
3·35	3·75	4·10	4·75

3. If v is less than v_c, nominal shear reinforcement should be provided throughout the span of beam such that for high-yield links

$$A_{sv}/s_v = 0\!\cdot\!0012b_t$$

For mild steel $A_{sv}/s_v = 0\!\cdot\!002b_t$

4. Where v is greater than v_c, shear reinforcement should be provided such that the ratio of A_{sv} and

Table 4.5   Ultimate shear stresses (N/mm^2) in beams for various concrete grades and values of $100A_s/bd$

$100A_s/bd$	Concrete grade			
	20	25	30	40 or more
0·25	0·35	0·35	0·35	0·35
0·30	0·37	0·38	0·39	0·39
0·35	0·39	0·41	0·43	0·43
0·40	0·41	0·44	0·47	0·47
0·45	0·43	0·47	0·51	0·51
0·50	0·45	0·50	0·55	0·55
0·55	0·46	0·51	0·56	0·57
0·60	0·48	0·53	0·58	0·59
0·65	0·49	0·54	0·59	0·61
0·70	0·51	0·56	0·61	0·63
0·75	0·52	0·57	0·62	0·65
0·80	0·54	0·59	0·64	0·67
0·85	0·55	0·60	0·65	0·69
0·90	0·57	0·62	0·67	0·71
0·95	0·58	0·63	0·68	0·73
1·00	0·60	0·65	0·70	0·75
1·05	0·61	0·66	0·71	0·76
1·10	0·62	0·67	0·72	0·77
1·15	0·63	0·68	0·73	0·78
1·20	0·64	0·69	0·74	0·79
1·25	0·65	0·70	0·75	0·80
1·30	0·66	0·71	0·76	0·81
1·35	0·67	0·72	0·77	0·82
1·40	0·68	0·73	0·78	0·83
1·45	0·69	0·74	0·79	0·84
1·50	0·70	0·75	0·80	0·85
1·55	0·71	0·76	0·81	0·86
1·60	0·72	0·77	0·82	0·87
1·65	0·73	0·78	0·83	0·88
1·70	0·74	0·79	0·84	0·89
1·75	0·75	0·80	0·85	0·90
1·80	0·76	0·81	0·86	0·91
1·85	0·77	0·82	0·87	0·92
1·90	0·78	0·83	0·88	0·93
1·95	0·79	0·84	0·89	0·94
2·00	0·80	0·85	0·90	0·95
3·00	0·85	0·90	0·95	1·00

Table 4.6   Shear resistance* of link with $f_{yv} = 250$ N/mm^2

s_v	Diameters				
	6	8	10	12	16
75	164	293	456	657	1168
100	123	220	342	492	876
125	98	176	273	394	702
150	82	146	228	328	584
175	70	125	195	281	501
200	61	110	171	246	438
250	49	88	136	197	351
300	41	73	114	164	292
350	35	63	98	141	250
400	31	55	85	123	219
450	26	49	76	109	195
500	25	44	68	98	175
550	22	40	62	89	159
600	21	37	57	82	146
700	18	31	49	70	125

* Values in newtons per millimetre depth of beam.

s_v satisfies the following conditions for shear resistance:

$$\frac{A_{sv}}{s_v} \geq \frac{b(v - v_c)}{0.87 f_{yv}}$$

Tables 4.6–4.8 tabulate values which, when multiplied by the depth of the beam (mm), give the shear resistance for particular values of A_{sv} and s_v.

5. The spacing of vertical links in the direction of span (s_v) and at right angles to the span should not exceed $0.75d$.

6. It is not necessary to provide shear reinforcement in slabs, bases, pile caps and similar members if v does not exceed v_c.

7. Up to 50% of shear reinforcement may be in the form of inclined bars. The shear resistance of one bar is $A_s \times 0.87 f_y \sin \theta$ where θ = the angle of inclination.

Table 4.7 Shear resistance* of links with $f_{yv} = 410$ N/mm²

s_v	Diameters				
	6	8	10	12	16
75	269	480	748	1078	1916
100	202	360	561	809	1438
125	161	288	448	647	1149
150	135	240	374	539	957
175	115	206	321	462	811
200	101	180	280	404	718
250	81	144	224	323	575
300	67	120	187	269	479
350	58	103	160	231	411
400	50	90	140	202	359
450	45	80	125	180	319
500	40	72	112	162	287
550	37	66	102	147	261
600	34	60	93	135	239
700	29	51	80	115	205

* Values in newtons per millimetre depth of beam.

Table 4.8 Shear resistance* of links with $f_{yv} = 425$ N/mm²

s_v	Diameters				
	6	8	10	12	16
75	279	498	774	1114	1982
100	209	373	580	836	1486
125	167	299	464	668	1189
150	140	249	387	557	991
175	120	213	332	447	849
200	105	187	290	418	743
250	84	149	232	334	595
300	70	124	193	278	495
350	60	107	166	239	425
400	52	93	145	209	372
450	47	83	129	186	330
500	42	75	116	167	297
550	38	68	105	152	270
600	35	62	97	139	248
700	30	53	83	119	212

* Values in newtons per millimetre depth of beam.

Deflection of rectangular beams

For all normal cases, the deflection of a beam will not be excessive if the ratio of its span to its effective depth is not greater than the appropriate ratio obtained from Tables 4.9 and 4.10. The use of Table 4.9 will restrict the deflection to approximately 1/250 of the span. Table 4.9 may be used for calculations relating to beams with a span of more than

Table 4.9 Basic span/depth ratios for rectangular beams not exceeding 10 m span*

Support condition	Ratio
Cantilever	7
Simply supported	20
Continuous	26

* This table should only be used for spans greater than 10 m if a deflection of span/250 is acceptable; when it is necessary to restrict the deflection further Table 4.10 should be used for spans exceeding 10 m.

Table 4.10 Basic span/depth ratios for rectangular beams exceeding 10 m span*

Span (m)	Cantilever	Simply supported	Continuous
10		20	26
12	To be	18	23
14	justified	18	21
16	by	14	18
18	calculation	12	16
20		10	13

* See footnote to Table 4.9.

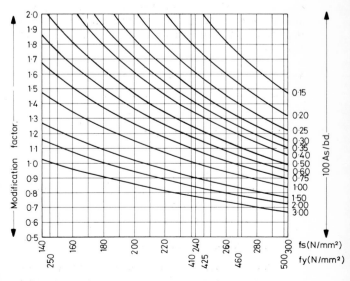

Figure 4.1 Modification factor for tension reinforcement

10 m if the deflection is acceptable; otherwise it is necessary to use the values from Table 4.10.

Values of the span/effective depth ratio should be multiplied by the appropriate factor obtained from Figure 4.1 or Table 4.11.

Table 4.11   Modification factor for compression reinforcement

$100A_s'/bd$	Factor	$100A_s'/bd$	Factor
0·25	1·07	1·50	1·33
0·50	1·14	2·00	1·40
0·75	1·20	3·00	1·50
1·00	1·25		

The minimum effective depth d of a rectangular beam with tension reinforcement only that will comply with the requirements of CP 110 Part 1: 1972 may be written as

$$\frac{\text{Effective span}}{(\text{factor, T.4.9 or T.4.10})(\text{factor, Fig. 4.1})}$$

where T.4.9 and T.4.10 indicate Table 4.9 and Table 4.10 respectively. The minimum effective depth d of a rectangular beam with tension and compression reinforcement that will comply with the requirements of CP 110 Part 1: 1972 may be written as

$$\frac{\text{Effective span}}{(\text{factor, T.4.9 or T.4.10})(\text{factor Fig. 4.1})(\text{factor T.4.11})}$$

where T.4.9, T.4.10 and T.4.11 indicate Tables 4.9, 4.10 and 4.11 respectively.

Deflection of flanged beams
For a flanged beam the span/effective depth ratio may be determined as above but the final ratio obtained should be multiplied by a factor obtained from Figure 4.2 where b_w = the breath of the web and b_c = the effective width of the flange (see page 63)

Anchorage bond
1. Bars in tension should extend beyond any section so that the anchorage bond stress at that section

Table 4.12   Ultimate anchorage bar stresses (N/mm²)

Bar type	Concrete grade			
	20	25	30	40 or more
Plain bar (tension)	1·2	1·4	1·5	1·9
Plain bar (compression)	1·5	1·7	1·9	2·3
Deformed bar (tension)	1·7	1·9	2·2	2·6
Deformed bar (compression)	2·1	2·4	2·7	3·2

In certain cases, if type-2 deformed reinforcement is used, the allowable bond stress may be increased by 30%.

Table 4.13   Ultimate local bond stresses (N/mm²)

Bar type	Concrete grade			
	20	25	30	40 or more
Plain bars	1·7	2·0	2·2	2·7
Deformed bars	2·1	2·5	2·8	3·4

In certain cases, if type-2 deformed reinforcement is used, the allowable bond stress may be increased by 20%

does not exceed that permitted in Table 4.12. This is satisfied if the length from that section is not less than

$$\text{Bar dia.} \times \frac{0·87f_y}{4 \times \text{UABS}}$$

where UABS is the ultimate anchorage bond stress.
2. Bars in compression should extend beyond any section so that the ultimate anchorage bond stress at that section does not exceed that permitted in Table 4.12. This condition is satisfied if the anchorage length from that section is not less than

$$\text{Bar dia.} \times \frac{2000f_y}{(2300 + f_y) \times 4 \times \text{UABS}}$$

where UABS is the ultimate anchorage bond strength.

Local bond
The ultimate local bond stress $V/\sum u_s d$ should not exceed the ultimate local bond stress given in Table 4.13.

Laps in bars
The length of lap should at least equal the anchorage length (see above) required to develop the stress in the smaller of the two bars lapped. When deformed bars are used, and the lap is in a tension zone, the length of lap is the anchorage length (based on the stress in the bar) times 1·25. The minimum lap lengths to be provided are

(a) Tension bars — 25 bar sizes plus 150 mm.
(b) Compression bars — 20 bar sizes plus 150 mm.

These lengths do not apply where main reinforcement is stopped and bars are provided as link supports only.

Curtailment of bars
In any member subject to bending, every curtailed bar should extend (except at end supports) beyond the calculated cut-off point for a distance equal to the effective depth of the member or 12 times the

bar size, whichever is greater. In addition, bars should not be stopped off in a tension zone unless one of the following conditions is satisfied:

(a) The bars extend an anchorage length appropriate to their design stress ($0.87f_y$).
(b) The shear capacity of the section, where the reinforcement stops, is greater than twice the shear force present.
(c) The continuing bars where reinforcement stops provide double the area required for the moment at such points.

At a simply supported end of a member, one of the following requirements should be fulfilled:

(a) Effective anchorage equivalent to 12 bar sizes beyond the centre line of support (no hook or bend should begin before the centre of the support).
(b) Effective anchorage equivalent to 12 bar sizes plus $d/2$ from the face of the support (no bend should begin $d/2$ from the face of the support).
(c) Provided that the local bond stress at the face of a support is less than half the value given in Table 4.13, a straight length of bar beyond the centre line of the support equal to either 1/3 the support width or 30 mm, whichever is greater, should be provided.

Simplified rules for the curtailment of bars are given in CP 110 Part 1: 1972 (3.11.7.2.)

Hooks and bends

The effective anchorage length of a hook or bend should be measured from the start of the bend to a point 4 times the bar size beyond the end of the bend. This may be taken as the lesser of 24 times the bar size, or

(a) For a hook — 8 times the internal radius of the hook.
(b) For a 90° bend — 4 times the internal radius of the bend.

Table 4.14 Nominal concrete cover (mm) to reinforcement

Conditions of exposure*	Concrete grade			
	25	30	40	50
Mild	20	15	15	15
Moderate	40	30	25	20
Severe	50	40	30	25

* For definitions of the conditions of exposure reference should be made to CP 110 Part 1: 1972.

Cover to reinforcement

General rules for reinforcement covers are given in CP 110 Part 1: 1972 (3.11.2). The nominal cover to any reinforcement should never be less than the bar size or 15 mm, whichever is greater. These covers are applicable to the reinforcement nearest the face of the member. Table 4.14 gives the normal range of conditions of exposure and the required nominal cover to the reinforcement.

In the above context bar size can be defined as follows:

(a) Individual bars — not less than the diameter of the bar.
(b) Pair of bars — not less than the diameter of the larger bar (where the diameters are unequal).
(c) Bundles of bars — not less than the diameter of a single bar of equivalent area.

Minimum distance between bars

The lateral dimension between bars should be the maximum-sized aggregate plus 5 mm or the bar size, whichever is the greater. The vertical dimension between bars should be 2/3 of the maximum-sized aggregate plus 5 mm.

Maximum distance between bars in tension

General rules for establishing the maximum distance between bars in tension are given in CP 110 Part 1: 1972 (3.11.8.2).

Table 4.15 Areas of reinforcement (mm^2) for beams and columns

Dia. (mm)	Mass (kg/m)	Number of bars in group											
		1	2	3	4	5	6	7	8	9	10	11	12
6	0.222	28	57	85	113	142	170	198	226	255	283	311	340
8	0.395	50	101	151	201	252	302	352	402	453	503	553	604
10	0.616	79	157	236	314	392	471	550	628	707	785	864	942
12	0.888	113	226	339	452	566	679	792	905	1 020	1 130	1 240	1 360
16	1.579	201	402	603	804	1 010	1 210	1 410	1 610	1 801	2 010	2 210	2 410
20	2.466	314	628	943	1 260	1 570	1 890	2 200	2 510	2 830	3 140	3 460	3 770
25	3.854	491	982	1 470	1 960	2 450	2 950	3 440	3 930	4 420	4 910	5 400	5 890
32	6.313	804	1 610	2 410	3 220	4 020	4 830	5 630	6 430	7 240	8 040	8 850	9 650
40	9.864	1 260	2 510	3 770	5 030	6 280	7 540	8 800	10 100	11 300	12 600	13 800	15 100
50	15.413	1 960	3 390	5 890	7 850	9 820	11 800	13 700	15 700	17 700	19 600	21 600	23 600

Table 4.16 Areas of reinforcement (mm²) for slabs and walls

Dia. (mm)	Centre-to-centre distance in mm									Perimeter (mm)
	50	75	100	125	150	175	200	250	300	
6	566	377	283	226	189	162	142	113	94	18·9
8	1 010	671	503	402	335	287	252	201	168	25·2
10	1 570	1 050	785	628	523	449	393	314	262	31·4
12	2 260	1 510	1 130	905	745	646	566	452	377	37·6
16	4 020	2 680	2 010	1 610	1 340	1 150	1 010	804	670	50·3
20	6 280	4 190	3 140	2 510	2 090	1 800	1 570	1 260	1 050	62·8
25	9 820	6 550	4 910	3 930	3 270	2 810	2 450	1 960	1 640	78·5
32	16 100	10 700	8 040	6 430	5 360	4 600	4 020	3 220	2 680	100·0
40	25 100	16 800	12 600	10 100	8 380	7 180	6 280	5 030	4 190	125·6
50	39 200	26 200	19 600	15 700	13 100	11 200	9 800	7 850	6 550	157·0

Reinforcement area tables

Reinforced concrete design calculations usually end with an area of reinforcement required.

For columns beams and other similar structural members the reinforcement required at any section will be quoted in mm². This has to be translated into a certain number of bars of given diamters. If, for example, a column required 2500 mm² of reinforcement, then it can be seen from Table 4.15 that eight 20 mm bars would be suitable, as their total cross-sectional area is 2510 mm².

In the case of slabs and other similar structural forms the required reinforcement will be specified in mm² per metre width. For example, if a slab required 600 mm²/m, then from Table 4.16 12 mm bars at 175 mm centre to centre would seem to be appropriate as their total cross-sectional area is 646 mm²/m width.

4.2 BASIC PRINCIPLES FOR THE DESIGN OF SOLID SLABS AND RECTANGULAR BEAMS

Assumptions

1. Plane sections remain plane in bending.
2. The tensile strength of concrete is ignored.
3. The stress distribution in the concrete in compression is derived from the stress–strain curve shown in CP 110 Part 1: 1972 (Figure 1).
4. The stress in the reinforcement is derived from the stress–strain curve shown in CP 110 Part 1: 1972 (Figure 2).

Basis of design

To find the amount of reinforcement required in a beam, the following methods can be used:

(a) Design charts.
(b) Design formulae.
(c) Strain compatibility.

Design charts have been prepared using the true parabolic stress block shown in Figure 4.3(c) and

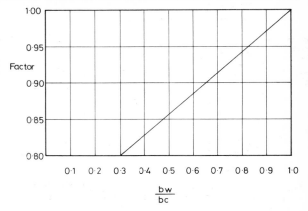

Figure 4.2 Modification factor for flanged beams

the stress–strain curves for reinforcement. These charts are to be found in CP 110 Part 2: 1972. They are for particular grades of concrete and strength of reinforcement. A typical chart is shown in Figure 4.4. The methods of design by formulae and strain compatibility are not included in this book.

Ultimate moments of resistance

$M_u(\text{concrete}) = 0{\cdot}15 f_{cu} b d^2$

$M_u(\text{reinforcement}) = (0{\cdot}87 f_y) A_s z$

These moments of resistance have been prepared using the simplified rectangular stress block as shown in Figure 4.3. The maximum value of z is $\frac{3}{4}d$ in this case. The moment of resistance of the section at the ultimate limit state must be equal to or greater than the ultimate applied bending moment.

4.3 SIMPLE SLAB DESIGN

Simply supported slab spanning in one direction

1. Decide on the material stresses to be used, i.e. f_{cu} and f_y.
2. Determine the overall thickness h of slab.

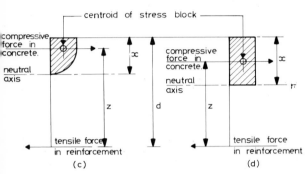

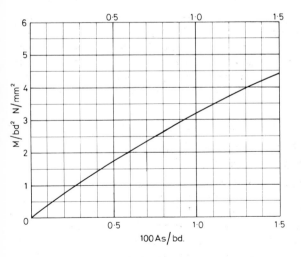

Figure 4.3 (a) Cross section through beam; (b) strain diagram; (c) true parabolic stress block; (d) simplified rectangular stress block

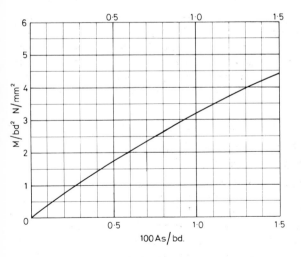

Characteristic strength of reinforcement $f_y = 425 \text{N/mm}^2$

Characteristic strength of concrete $f_{cu} = 30 \text{N/mm}^2$

Figure 4.4 Typical design chart for single reinforced beam

(a) Assume a maximum value for $100A_s/bd$ say 0·5 for high-yield reinforcement or 0·6 for mild steel reinforcement.

(b) Obtain the modification factor (Figure 4.1).
(c) Select the basic ratio (Table 4.9 or 4.10).
(d) Calculate the allowable ratio = basic ratio × modification factor.

(e) $d = \dfrac{\text{Effective span}}{\text{Allowable ratio}}$

(f) Overall thickness $h = d$ + appropriate concrete cover (Table 4.14) + $\frac{1}{2}$(bar size).
(g) Adjust the overall thickness to practical dimension.

3. Estimate the characteristic loads g_k and q_k per unit area.
4. Calculate the design loads $1\cdot4g_k$ and $1\cdot6q_k$ per unit area.
5. Determine the ultimate bending moment M.
6. Check the effective depth d.
7. Check the overall thickness for appropriate fire resistance if necessary (see CP 110 Part 1: 1972).
8. Determine the ultimate resistance moment based on the concrete section.
9. Calculate M/bd^2 and determine $100A_s/bd$ from Figure 4.4 or from the appropriate design chart in CP 110 Part 2: 1972.
10. Select the reinforcement required from Table 4.16.
11. Determine the distribution reinforcement required; the minimum required is $0\cdot0012bh$ for high-yield reinforcement and $0\cdot0015bh$ for mild steel reinforcement where $b = 1000$ mm and $h =$ the overall depth of the slab.
12. The bar spacing (maximum) is to be in accordance with clause 3:11:8:2 of CP 110 Part 1: 1972.
13. A check on the span/depth ratio for the slab will not be necessary if the actual $100A_s/bd$ is less than 0·5 or 0·6 depending on the reinforcement type used.

Simply supported slab spanning in two directions

1. Decide on the material stresses to be used, i.e. f_{cu} and f_y.
2. Determine the overall thickness of the slab based on the shorter span.
   (a) assume a maximum value for $100A_s/bd$, say 0·4 for high-yield reinforcement or 0·5 for mild steel reinforcement.
   (b) Obtain the modification factor (Figure 4.1).
   (c) Select the basic ratio (Table 4.9 or 4.10).
   (d) Calculate the allowable ratio = basic ratio × modification factor.

(e) $d = \dfrac{\text{Effective short span}}{\text{Allowable ratio}}$

Table 4.17   Bending moment coefficients for slabs spanning in two directions, at right angles, simply supported on four sides

l_y/l_x	1·0	1·1	1·2	1·3	1·4	1·5	1·75	2·0	2·5	3·0
α_{sx}	0·062	0·074	0·084	0·093	0·099	0·104	0·113	0·118	0·122	0·124
α_{sy}	0·062	0·061	0·059	0·055	0·051	0·046	0·037	0·029	0·020	0·014

At least 50% of the tension reinforcement provided at mid-span should extend to the supports. The remaining 50% should extend to within $0·1\,l_x$ or $0·1\,l_y$ of the support, as appropriate.

(f) Overall thickness $h = d +$ appropriate concrete cover (Table 4.14) $+ \frac{1}{2}$(bar size).

(g) Adjust the overall thickness to practical dimension.

3. Estimate the characteristic loads g_k and q_k per unit area.

4. Calculate the design load $n = 1·4g_k + 1·6q_k$.

5. Determine the ultimate bending moments in the short and long spans from:

Short span, $M_{sx} = \alpha_{sx}nl_x^2$

Long span, $M_{sy} = \alpha_{sy}nl_x^2$

where M_{sx} and $M_{sy} =$ the moments at mid-span on strips of unit width and spans l_x and l_y, $n =$ the total ultimate load per unit area ($1·4g_k + 1·6q_k$), $l_y =$ the length of the longer side, $l_x =$ the length of the shorter span, and α_{sx} and $\alpha_{sy} =$ the moment coefficients shown in Table 4.17.

6. Check the effective depth d for the short span and the long span (see Figure 4.5).

7. Check the overall thickness h for appropriate fire resistance if necessary (see CP 110 Part 1: 1972).

8. Calculate M/bd^2 for the short and long span and determine $100A_s/bd$ from Figure 4.4 or from the appropriate design chart in CP 110 Part 2: 1972.

9. Select the reinforcement required from Table 4.16.

10. The bar spacing (maximum) is to be in accordance with clause 3:11:8:2 of CP 110 Part 1: 1972.

11. A check of the span/depth ratio for the slab will not be necessary if the actual $100A_s/bd$ is less than 0·4 or 0·5 depending on the reinforcement type used.

4.4 SIMPLE BEAM DESIGN

Simply supported rectangular beam with tension reinforcement only

1. Decide on the material stresses to be used, i.e. f_{cu} and f_y.

2. Assume a size of beam.

3. Estimate the characteristic loads g_k and q_k per unit length of beam.

4. Calculate the design loads $1·4g_k$ and $1·6q_k$ per unit length of beam.

5. Determine the ultimate bending moment M.

6. Choose the appropriate concrete cover from Table 4.14 and determine d.

7. Check cover is appropriate for fire resistance if necessary (see CP 110 Part 1: 1972).

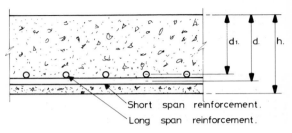

 d = effective depth (short span)
 d_1 = effective depth (long span)
 h = overall depth

Figure 4.5   Two-way spanning slabs

8. Determine the ultimate resistance moment based on the concrete section (this must be equal to, or greater than, the ultimate bending moment, otherwise a larger section or compression reinforcement must be considered).

9. Calculate M/bd^2 and determine $100A_s/bd$ from Figure 4.4 or from the appropriate design chart in CP 110 Part 2: 1972.

10. Select the reinforcement required from Table 4.15.

11. Check the span/depth ratio.

(a) Calculate the actual $100A_s/bd$ and obtain the modification factor from Figure 4.1.

(b) Select the basic ratio (Table 4.9 or 4.10).

(c) Calculate the allowable ratio = basic ratio × modification factor.

(d) Actual ratio $= \dfrac{\text{Effective span}}{\text{Effective depth}}$

(e) The actual ratio must be less than the allowable ratio.

12. Calculate the shear reinforcement.

(a) Calculate the actual shear stress v.

(b) Determine $100A_s/bd$ ($A_s =$ minimum tension reinforcement allowing for curtailments) and find v_c from Table 4.5. If $v_c < v$, provide shear reinforcement.

(c) Calculate the bar size and spacing for nominal links if $v_c > v$ or

(d) If $v_c < v$. Shear stress resistance of beam
= Shear resistance of concrete + shear resistance of links
= $v_c b_t d +$ value from Table 4.6, 4.7 or 4.8 × effective depth.

(e) If the shear resistance of the beam is less than the ultimate applied shearing force V, draw a shear force diagram and work out the stopping-off points for shear links.

(f) Calculate $b_t(v - v_c)$ and select from Tables 4.6, 4.7 or 4.8 the suitable bar size and spacings of links.

13. Local bond stress must not exceed the values given in Table 4.13.

4.5 BASIC PRINCIPLES FOR THE DESIGN OF SIMPLY SUPPORTED FLANGED BEAMS WITH TENSION REINFORCEMENT ONLY

Introduction

Most beams form part of a floor arrangement in which the reinforced concrete floor is monolithic with the beam. Part of the floor acts as the com-

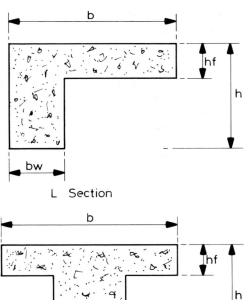

L Section

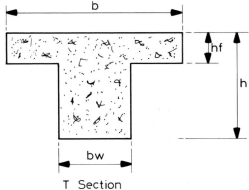

T Section

h   = overall depth
bw = breadth of rib (or web)
b   = effective width
hf = overall depth of slab (or flange)

Figure 4.6 Flanged beams

pression zone for the beam, thus increasing the load capacity of the member. Details of the two most common types of flanged beams are shown in Figure 4.6.

Effective width of flange

For a 'T' beam, it is the lesser of:
(a) The width of the rib + 1/5 of the distance between points of zero moment.
(b) The actual width of the flange.
For an 'L' beam, it is the lesser of:
(a) The width of the rib + 1/10 of the distance between points of zero moment.
(b) The actual width of the flange.

Assumptions

These are stated in 4.2 but are repeated here.
1. Plane sections remain plane in bending.
2. The tensile strength of concrete is ignored.
3. The stress distribution in the concrete in compression is derived from the stress–strain curve shown in CP 110 Part 1: 1972 (Figure 1).
4. The stress in the reinforcement is derived from the stress–strain curve shown in CP 110 Part 1: 1972 (Figure 2).

Basis of design

To find the amount of reinforcement required in a flanged beam one of the following methods can be adopted:
(a) Design charts.
(b) Design formulae.
(c) Strain compatibility.

Design charts may be used for the design of flanged beams providing the depth to the neutral axis lies within the thickness of the flange. The most usual way to design a flanged beam is to take advantage of the simplified formulae in CP 110 Part 1: 1972. In this case the ultimate resistance moments are

$$M_u(\text{concrete}) = 0 \cdot 4f_{cu}bh_f(d - h_f/2)$$
$$M_u(\text{reinforcement}) = (0 \cdot 87f_y)A_s(d - h_f/2)$$

Strain compatibility is not considered in this book.

4.6 SIMPLE FLANGED BEAM DESIGN

Simply supported flanged beam with tension reinforcement only

1. Decide on the material stresses to be used, i.e. f_{cu} and f_y.
2. Assume an overall depth and breadth of rib.

3. Estimate the characteristic loads g_k and q_k per unit length of beam.

4. Calculate the design loads $1.4g_k$ and $1.6q_k$ per unit length of beam.

5. Determine the ultimate bending moment M.

6. Calculate the maximum permissible width of the flange.

7. Choose the appropriate concrete cover from Table 4.14 and determine d.

8. Check that the cover is appropriate for fire resistance if necessary (see Cp 110 Part 1: 1972).

9. Determine the ultimate resistance moment based on the concrete section (this must be equal to, or greater than, the ultimate bending moment, otherwise a larger section or compression reinforcement must be considered).

10. Calculate the reinforcement required from

$$A_s = \frac{M}{0.87f_y \times (d - h_f/2)}$$

11. Select the reinforcement required from Table 4.15.

12. Check the span/depth ratio.

  (a) Calculate the actual $100A_s/bd$ and obtain the modification factor from Figure 4.1 (b = effective flange width).

  (b) Select the basic ratio (Table 4.9 or 4.10).

  (c) Obtain the flange modification factor (Figure 4.2).

  (d) Calculate the allowable ratio = basic ratio × modification factors.

  (e) Actual ratio = Effective span/Effective depth.

  (f) The actual ratio must be less than the allowable ratio.

13. Calculate the shear and nominal reinforcement (see 4.4). The beam breadth in this case is taken as the breadth of rib.

14. Local bond stress must not exceed the values given in Table 4.13.

4.7 SIMPLY SUPPORTED HOLLOW BLOCK SLAB DESIGN

Introduction

CP 110: 1972 defines this type of slab as a series of concrete ribs, cast *in situ*, between blocks which remain part of the complete structure (Figure 4.7). The tops of the ribs are usually connected by a concrete topping of the same strength as that used in the ribs. Although the code suggests that under certain stated conditions the blocks can contribute to the thickness of the structural topping and breadth of rib, in the treatment given here the

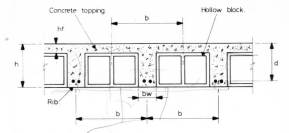

Figure 4.7   A hollow block slab

hollow blocks are not regarded as contributing to the structural strength and slip tiles are not considered. As the size and weights of blocks vary, an accurate weight of floor should be worked out from trade literature.

Design

1. Decide on the material stresses to be used, i.e. f_{cu} and f_y.

2. Assume a size of block, thickness of structural concrete topping and breadth of rib.

3. Calculate the maximum permissible width of flange (usually taken at the centres of ribs).

4. Calculate the characteristic loads g_k and q_k per unit length of slab per width of flange.

5. Calculate the design loads $1.4 g_k$ and $1.6 q_k$ per unit length of slab per width of flange.

6. Determine the ultimate bending moment M.

7. Choose the appropriate concrete cover from Table 4.14.

8. Check that the overall thickness is appropriate for fire resistance if necessary (see CP 110 Part 1: 1972).

9. Determine the ultimate resistance moment based on the concrete section (this must be equal to, or greater than, the ultimate bending moment, otherwise a larger section must be considered).

10. Calculate the reinforcement required in the rib from

$$A_s = \frac{M}{0.87f_y(d - h_f/2)}$$

11. Select the reinforcement required from Table 4.15.

12. Check the span/depth ratio (see 4.6).

13. Check the shear stress. The critical point for shear is usually at the edge of the hollow block and solid concrete section. The shear will be taken on the rib only. CP 110: 1972 recommends that shear reinforcement is not provided in slabs.

  (a) Calculate the shear force V at the edge of the hollow block section.

  (b) Determine the actual shear stress v.

(c) Determine the allowable shear stress v_c.
(d) If $v_c > v$, then the slab is suitable.
(e) If $v_c < v$, it may be necessary to adjust the critical point for shear so that the value of v is decreased below the value of v_c.
14. Local bond stress must not exceed the values given in Table 4.13.

4.8 SIMPLE COLUMN BASE DESIGN

Introduction
The thickness of the base must be sufficient to resist the shearing forces and bending moments safely. The allowable bearing pressure of the soil under the base is normally determined from tests on soil samples. CP 2004: 1972 provides a guide to the allowable bearing pressures which can be used for the preliminary design of the base. The size of the base should be determined using the column serviceability loading. The design of the reinforcement for the base should be carried out using ultimate limit state.

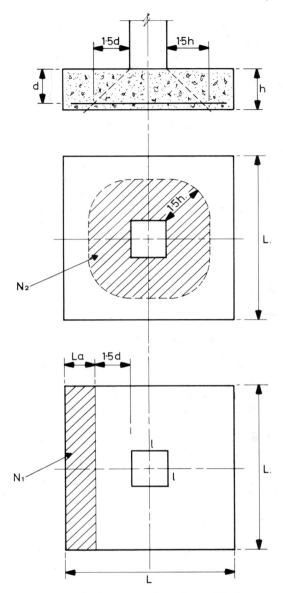

Figure 4.8 A simple square column base, with plans showing the load within the critical shear perimeter and the load against transverse shear

Design of square base with concentric column load only (Figure 4.8)
A plan area of base ($L \times L$)
A_1 area within critical shear perimeter
d effective depth of tension reinforcement
h overall thickness of base
N_s axial column load (service)
N_u axial column load (ultimate)
N_1 load against transverse shear
N_2 load within area of critical perimeter
N_3 load against punching
M ultimate bending moment
p critical shear perimeter
q_s allowable bearing pressure of soil (service)
q_u actual bearing pressure of soil (ultimate)
v_1 actual transverse shear stress
v_2 actual punching shear stress

1. Convert 'design' column load to 'service' condition ($1.0G_K + 1.0Q_K$).
2. Assume a thickness, and determine the weight of base per square metre (kN/m²).
3. Determine the net allowable bearing pressure $= q_s -$ weight of base (kN/m²).
4. Calculate the area of base required

$$= \frac{N_s}{\text{net allowable bearing pressure}} \text{ (m}^2\text{)}$$

5. Determine side L (m).
6. Calculate $q_u = N_u/A$ (kN/m²).
7. Choose the appropriate concrete cover from Table 4.14 and determine $d = h - (\text{cover} + \frac{1}{2}$ bar diameter).
8. Calculate $N_1 = q_u \times L \times L_a$ (kN).
9. Choose the material stresses to be used (if not already decided).
10. Determine $v_1 = N_1/Ld$ (N/mm²).

11. Calculate $p = 4l + 3\pi h$ (mm).

12. Calculate $A_1 = l^2 + \pi(1\cdot5h)^2 + 4(1\cdot5h \times l)$ (m²).

13. Determine $N_2 = q_u \times A_1$ (kN).

14. Determine $N_3 = N_u - N_2$ (kN).

15. Calculate $v_2 = N_3/(p \times d)$ (N/mm²).

16. Obtain $100A_s/bd$ for the worst case of shear (v_1 or v_2) from Table 4.5.

17. Calculate M

$$= \frac{N_u}{8L}(L - 1)^2 \text{ (N mm)}$$

18. Calculate M/bd^2 and obtain $100A_s/bd$ from figure 4.4. or the appropriate design chart.

19. Determine the area of reinforcement required for the worst case of $100A_s/bd$ (16 or 18).

20. Select the reinforcement required from Table 4.15 (same in both directions).

21. Local bond stress must not exceed the values given in Table 4.13.

5 Prestressed concrete

5.1 INTRODUCTION

The design procedures for all but the simplest of prestressed concrete members do not lend themselves, for the purposes of this book, to a simplified approach. However, the underlying structural principle of prestressing is in itself relatively simple. To illustrate this point an abbreviated design example for a simply supported beam of rectangular cross section will be used.

In the context of structural concrete, prestressing is a term applied to those methods of construction where the flexural tension stresses due to dead and imposed loads are balanced, or significantly reduced by the application of a compressive force. This force is induced through high-strength steel or alloy tendons running through the length of the member. The advantage over normal reinforced concrete of this system is that the full compressive strength of the concrete is utilised under working conditions across the greater part of the cross section of the member. The deflection of the member is also minimised. It is though, in comparison, a costly method of construction and tends therefore to be used in certain specialised cases only.

In specific terms there are two methods of achieving the prestressing effect. These are pre-tensioning and post-tensioning. In the case of pre-tensioning, the tendons are first stressed by the application of a tensioning force. The concrete is then cast around the tendons. When the concrete has achieved the required strength the tendons are severed at the ends of the member. The tensile stress in the tendons being resisted by a compressive stress in the concrete through the bond between the tendons and the concrete, this form of prestressing is often used in the production of factory-made units such as floor beams. With post-tensioning, ducts are cast in the concrete element through which the tendons are passed. After the concrete has reached a specified strength the tendons are stressed and anchored at their ends to the member. This has the effect of setting up a compressive stress in the concrete. This method is normally used for larger structures such as bridge, deck beams etc. In both cases the force in the tendons is produced by using a hydraulic jack. When this force is applied to the concrete it is termed the 'transfer of stress'. For pre-tensioned members this occurs when the tendons are severed. In post-tensioned work it occurs as soon as the tendons are stressed.

5.2 DESIGN REQUIREMENTS FROM CP 110: 1972, 'THE STRUCTURAL USE OF CONCRETE'

Concrete
In order to take full advantage of prestressing, high-strength concrete must be used. The characteristic

Table 5.2   Compressive stresses for concrete in service

Nature of loading	Allowable compressive stresses*
Design load in bending	$0.33f_{cu}$ (for simply supported beams)
Design load in direct compression	$0.25f_{cu}$

* f_{cu}, characteristic concrete cube strength.

Table 5.3   Allowable compressive stresses at transfer

Nature of stress distribution	Allowable compressive stress*
Triangular or near-triangular distribution of prestress	$0.5f_{ci}$
Uniform or near-uniform distribution of prestress	$0.4f_{ci}$

* f_{ci}, concrete strength at transfer.

Table 5.1   Strength of concrete

Grade	Characteristic strength (N/mm^2)	Cube strength in N/mm^2 at age of				
		7 days	2 months	3 months	6 months	1 year
30	30·0	20	33	35	36	37
40	40·0	28	44	45·5	47·5	50
50	50·0	36	54	55·5	57·5	60
60	60·0	45	64*	65·5*	67·5*	70*

* These increased strengths due to age should only be used if it has been demonstrated to the satisfaction of the engineer that the materials to be used are capable of producing these higher strengths.

strengths normally specified are shown in Table 5.1. When prestressed concrete members are in service the compressive strength of the concrete should not exceed the values given in Table 5.2. The allowable compressive strength of the concrete at transfer of stress is usually greater than the concrete strength in service (see also 'Loss of prestress'.). Values of allowable compressive strengths at transfer are given in Table 5.3. In some cases tensile stresses in flexure are permitted. Reference should, however, be made to the relevant section of CP 110: 1972.

Steel

The steel used in prestressing work is usually in the form of high-tensile wires or alloy steel bars.

Definition of terms

Tendon. A stretched element used in a concrete member to impart prestress to the concrete; can consist of individual steel wires, bars or strands.
Cables. A group of tendons.
Wires. Reinforcement of solid cross section up to 7 mm in diameter complying with the requirements of BS 2691: 1969.
Strands. A group of either 7 or 19 wires wound in helical form complying with the requirements of BS 3617: 1971 and BS 4757: 1971.
Bars. Reinforcement of solid cross section up to 40 mm in diameter complying with the requirements of BS 4456: 1969.

Values of characteristic strength for wires, strands and bars are given in Tables 5.4–5.6.

Table 5.4   Specified characteristic strengths of prestressing wire

Nominal size (mm)	Specified characteristic strength (kN)	Nominal cross-sectional area (mm²)
2	6·34	3·14
2·65	10·3	5·5
3	12·2	7·1
3·25	14·3	8·3
4	21·7	12·6
4·5	25·7	15·9
5	30·8	19·6
7	60·4	38·5

Table 5.5   Specified characteristic strengths of prestressing bars

Nominal size (mm)	Specified characteristic strength (kN)	Nominal cross-sectional area (mm²)
20*	325	314
22	375	380
25*	500	491
28	625	615
32*	800	804
35	950	961
40*	1250	1257

* Preferred sizes.

Table 5.6   Specified characteristic strengths of prestressing strands

Number of wires	Nominal size (mm)	Specified characteristic strength (kN)	Nominal cross-sectional area (mm²)
7	6·4	44·5	24·5
	7·9	69·0	37·4
	9·3	93·5	52·3
	10·9	125	71·0
	12·5	165	94·2
	15·2	227	138·7
19	18	370	210
	25·4	659	423
	28·6	823	535
	31·8	979	660

Loss of prestress

There are a number of ways in which the initial prestressing force exerted by the jack is not effectively retained after transfer. This is known as loss of prestress. The causes can be summarised as follows:

(a) Shrinkage of concrete.
(b) Elastic deformation of concrete.
(c) Creep of concrete.
(d) Relaxation of steel.
(e) Steam curing.
(f) Friction.

Maximum initial prestress

The jacking force should not normally exceed 70% of the characteristic strength of the tendon. In some cases the force can be increased to 80%, but reference should be made to the relevant section of CP 110: 1972.

Cover

In general, the rules governing cover to reinforced concrete apply also to prestressed concrete, but reference should be made to the relevant section of CP 110: 1972.

Effective span

The effective span of a simply supported member should be taken as the smaller of

(i) The distance between the centres of bearings, or
(ii) The clear distance between supports, plus the effective depth.

5.3 DESIGN OF RECTANGULAR SIMPLY SUPPORTED PRE-TENSIONED BEAM (NO TENSION DEVELOPS)

Symbol

A cross-sectional area of beam (mm^2)
e eccentricity of prestressing force (mm)
f_{ci} allowable compressive stress for concrete at transfer (N/mm^2)
f_{cs} allowable compressive stress for concrete in service (N/mm^2)
M_d bending moment due to deadweight of beam (N mm)
M_1 bending moment due to additional dead and live loads (N mm)
M_s total service moment at any section $= M_d + M_1$ (N mm)
P prestressing force in tension (N)
Z section modulus (mm^3)
α $\dfrac{\text{Effective force in tendon after losses}}{\text{Force in tendon at transfer}}$

Procedure for preliminary calculations to determine the minimum required prestress force P(min) and the maximum eccentricity e(max) for a class-1 rectangular simply supported prestressed concrete beam

1. Calculate the maximum bending moment due to the superimposed live load:

$$M_1 = wl^2/8 \text{ (N mm)}$$

where w = the superimposed live load per metre run of beam and l = the effective span.

2. Assume a value for the maximum bending moment due to the self-weight of the beam, i.e. 35% of M_1;

i.e. $M_d = 0.35M_1$ (N mm)

3. Calculate the total service moment $M_s = M_d + M_1$.
4. Calculate the minimum section modulus Z_t required to keep within the allowable compression stress in the top fibre of the concrete in service:

$$Z_t = M_s/f_{cs}$$

For values of f_{cs} see Table 5.2.
5. Calculate the minimum section modulus Z_b required to keep within the allowable compression stress in the bottom fibre of the concrete due to the initial prestress:

$$Z_b = M_s/\alpha f_{ci}$$

For α assume a value of 0.8; for values of f_{ci} see Table 5.3.
6. A section for the beam must now be chosen based on the requirements of Z_t and Z_b. It is also necessary to check that the actual dead load moment M_d is less than, or equal to, the assumed value of $0.35M_1$. If the section chosen satisfies these conditions then:
7. Calculate the minimum required prestressing force

$$P(\text{min}) = \frac{(M_s - \alpha M_d)}{\alpha(Z_t + Z_b)}A \quad \text{(N)}$$

8. Calculate the maximum allowable eccentricity of the prestressing force

$$e(\text{max}) = Z_b/A + M_d/P(\text{min}) \quad \text{(mm)}$$

$\dfrac{P}{A}$

Direct stress due to prestress.

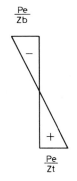

$\dfrac{Pe}{Zb}$

$\dfrac{Pe}{Zt}$

Bending stress due to prestress.

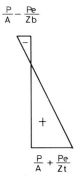

$\dfrac{P}{A} - \dfrac{Pe}{Zb}$

$\dfrac{P}{A} + \dfrac{Pe}{Zt}$

Combined direct and bending stress due to prestress.

$\dfrac{Md}{Zb}$

$\dfrac{Md}{Zt}$

Bending due to superimposed load.

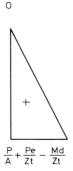

0

$\dfrac{P}{A} + \dfrac{Pe}{Zt} - \dfrac{Md}{Zt}$

Stress condition at moment of transfer.

Figure 5.1 Critical stress distributions in a concrete beam at moment of transfer

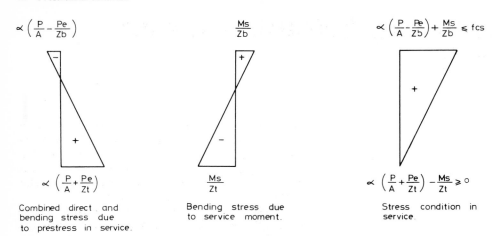

$$\propto \left(\frac{P}{A} - \frac{Pe}{Zb} \right)$$

$$\frac{Ms}{Zb}$$

$$\propto \left(\frac{P}{A} - \frac{Pe}{Zb} \right) + \frac{Ms}{Zb} \leqslant fcs$$

$$\propto \left(\frac{P}{A} + \frac{Pe}{Zt} \right)$$

$$\frac{Ms}{Zt}$$

$$\propto \left(\frac{P}{A} + \frac{Pe}{Zt} \right) - \frac{Ms}{Zt} \geqslant 0$$

Combined direct and bending stress due to prestress in service.

Bending stress due to service moment.

Stress condition in service.

Figure 5.2   Critical stress distribution in a concrete beam under service conditions

Figure 5.1 shows the critical stress distributions in the beam at the moment of transfer. Figure 5.2 shows the critical stress distributions in the beam under service conditions.

It is advised to check with the calculated values of P(min) and e(max) that the above conditions are satisfied.

It should be noted that these results are only preliminary and further calculations would be required to determine the actual loss of prestress (an assumption has been made at this stage). The requirements of ultimate limit state and deflection should also be satisfied.

6 Load-bearing brickwork and blockwork

6.1 DESIGN REQUIREMENTS

BS 5628 Part 1: 1978, *Structural use of masonry* gives recommendations for the design of unreinforced brickwork and blockwork. It is intended that this code will replace CP 111: 1970.

Limit state

This can be defined as the achievement of acceptable probabilities that the brick or block wall being designed will not become unfit for the use for which it is required.

Characteristic loads

Since it is not at present possible to express loads in statistical terms, the following characteristic loads should be included in the design:

(a) Dead loads G_k. The weight of the structure complete with finishes, partitions etc.
(b) Imposed loads Q_k. Weight due to furniture, occupants etc.
(c) Wind loads W_k.

The following publications should be used to compute the loads on the structure:

BS 648: 1964, *Schedule of weights of building materials.*
CP 3 Chapter V Part 1: 1967, *Dead and imposed loads.*
CP 3 Chapter V Part 2: 1972, *Wind loads.*

Characteristic strength of masonry

This is the value of the strength of masonry below which the probability of test results failing is not more than 5%. The characteristic compressive strength may be based on the results of laboratory tests or on information given in BS 5628 Part 1: 1978. Typical values of characteristic strength are given in Tables 6.1 and 6.2. (The mortar designations in these tables are given in Table 6.3.)

It should be noted that where the horizontal cross-sectional area of a loaded wall or column is less than 0.2 m^2 the characteristic compressive strength should be multiplied by the factor $(0.70 + 1.5A)$ where A = horizontal loaded cross-sectional area of the wall or column.

Partial safety factors

Loads. In this case partial safety factors are introduced to take account of unforeseen variations in the characteristic loads. The partial safety factors

Table 6.1 Characteristic compressive strength f_k of masonry constructed with standard format bricks

Mortar designation	Compressive strength of unit (N/mm²)								
	5	10	15	20	27.5	35	50	70	100
(i)	2.5	4.4	6.0	7.4	9.2	11.4	15.0	19.2	24.0
(ii)	2.5	4.2	5.3	6.4	7.9	9.4	12.2	15.1	18.3
(iii)	2.5	4.1	5.0	5.8	7.1	8.5	10.6	13.1	15.5
(iv)	2.2	3.5	4.4	5.2	6.2	7.3	9.0	10.8	12.6

Table 6.2 Characteristic compressive strength f_k of solid concrete blocks having a ratio of height to least horizontal dimension of between 2.0 and 4.0

Mortar designation	Compressive strength of unit (N/mm²)							
	2.8	3.5	5.0	7.0	10	15	20	35 or greater
(i)	2.8	3.5	5.0	6.8	8.8	12.0	14.8	22.8
(ii)	2.8	3.5	5.0	6.4	8.4	10.6	12.8	18.8
(iii)	2.8	3.5	5.0	6.4	8.2	10.0	11.6	17.0
(iv)	2.8	3.5	4.4	5.6	7.0	8.8	10.4	14.6

Table 6.3 Mortar mixes and strengths

Mortar designation	Type of mortar (proportion by volume)			Mean compressive strength (N/mm²) at 28 days	
	Cement:lime: sand	Masonry cement: sand	Cement:sand with plasticiser	Preliminary (laboratory) tests	Site tests
(i)	1:0-¼:3	–	–	16.0	11.0
(ii)	1:½:4-4½	1:2½-3½	1:3-4	6.5	4.5
(iii)	1:1:5-6	1:4-5	1:5-6	3.6	2.5
(iv)	1:2:8-9	1:5½-6½	1:7-8	1.5	1.0

Table 6.4   Partial safety factor γ_f for design loads

Loading	Partial safety factor

(a) Design and imposed load
  Design dead load
  Design imposed load
	$0.9G_k$ or $1.4G_k$
	$1.6Q_k$

(b) Dead and wind load
  Design dead load
  Design wind load
	$0.9G_k$ or $1.4G_k$
	$1.4W_k$ or $0.015G_k$ whichever is the greater

(c) Dead, imposed and wind load
  Design dead load
  Design imposed load
  Design wind load
	$1.2G_k$
	$1.2Q_k$
	$1.2W_k$ or $0.015G_k$ whichever is the greater

(d) Accidental damage
  Design dead load
  Design imposed load
 	
  Design wind load
	$0.95G_k$ or $1.05G_k$
	$0.35Q_k$ (except in the case of buildings used predominantly for storage, or where the imposed load is of a permanent nature, $1.05Q_k$ should be used)
	$0.35W_k$

NOTE.   1. Where alternative values are shown, that producing the most severe conditions should be selected.
2. In design, each of the combination (a)–(d) should be considered and that giving the most severe conditions should be adopted.
3. G_k, characteristic dead load.
   Q_k, characteristic imposed load.
   W_k, characteristic wind load.

Table 6.5   Partial safety factors γ_m for material strength

		Category of construction control*	
		Special	Normal
Category of manufacturing	Special	2.5	3.1
control of structural units	Normal	2.8	3.5

* For a description of categories of manufacturing and construction control see BS 5628 Part 1: 1978.

differ for dead, imposed and wind loads and are set out in Table 6.4.

Materials. Such safety factors are introduced to allow for possible differences between the characteristic strength and the actual structural strength. The values of these factors are generally taken as shown in Table 6.5; they allow for the difference between laboratory- and site-constructed brickwork and blockwork.

Design loads

These can be defined as

Characteristic load × partial safety factor.

As previously mentioned, the partial safety factors vary according to the circumstances under which the loads are considered. Maximum design loads can be obtained by reference to Table 6.4.

Effective height

The effective height of a wall may be taken as:

(a) 0·75 × the clear distance between lateral supports which provide enhanced resistance to lateral movement, or
(b) The clear distance between lateral supports which provide simple resistance to lateral movement.

The effective height of a column should be taken as

(a) The distance between lateral supports, or
(b) Twice that distance in respect of a direction in which lateral support is not provided.

The effective height of a pier may be treated as a wall for effective height consideration if the thickness of the pier is not greater than 1·5 times the thickness of the wall of which it forms a part. The pier should otherwise be treated as a column in the plane at right angles to the wall.

The terms 'enhanced' and 'simple' resistance are defined in BS 5628 Part 1: 1978. Examples are given in Figures 6.1 and 6.2.

Effective length

The effective length of a wall may be taken as

(a) 0·75 × the clear distance between vertical lateral supports, or

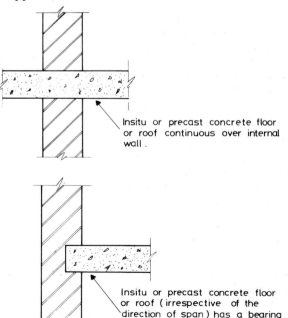

Insitu or precast concrete floor or roof continuous over internal wall.

Insitu or precast concrete floor or roof (irrespective of the direction of span) has a bearing of ½ wall thickness but in no case less than 90mm.

Figure 6.1   Examples of enhanced resistance to lateral movement of wall

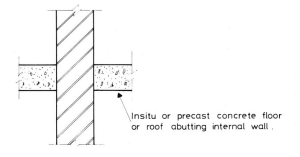

Insitu or precast concrete floor
or roof abutting internal wall.

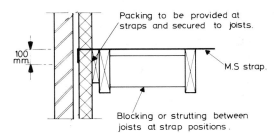

100
mm

Packing to be provided at
straps and secured to joists.

M.S strap.

Blocking or strutting between
joists at strap positions.

Figure 6.2 Examples of simple resistance to lateral movement
of wall (other examples of simple resistance are shown in
BS 5628 Part 1: 1978)

(b) Twice the distance between a support and a
free edge, where lateral supports provide enhanced
resistance to lateral movement, or
(c) The clear distance between lateral supports, or
(d) 2·5 × the distance between a support and a free
edge, where lateral supports provide simple resistance to lateral movement.

Effective thickness

The effective thickness of a single-leaf wall or
column is the actual thickness.

The effective thickness of a cavity wall or column
should be taken as

(a) $\frac{2}{3}(t_1 + t_2)$, or
(b) t_1, or
(c) t_2.

where t_1 and t_2 = the actual thickness of the brick
or block leaf.

When a wall is stiffened by piers or intersecting
walls the effective thickness of a single-leaf wall
(which may be one leaf of a cavity wall) is given
by

$$t_{ef} = t \times K$$

where t_{ef} = the effective thickness of the wall or leaf,
t = the actual thickness of the wall or leaf and
K = the appropriate stiffness coefficient taken from
Table 6.6.

Table 6.6 Stiffness coefficient K for walls stiffened by piers

Ratio of pier spacing (centre to centre) to pier width	*Ratio of pier thickness to actual thickness of wall to which it is bonded*		
	1	2	3
6	1·0	1·4	2·0
10	1·0	1·2	1·4
20	1·0	1·0	1·0

If intersecting walls are used to stiffen a wall
instead of piers, assume the intersecting wall to be
a pier, where b = the thickness of the intersecting
wall and t_p = 3 times the thickness of the stiffened
wall. The appropriate stiffness coefficient may then
be obtained from Table 6.6.

Slenderness ratio

This can be defined as

$$\frac{\text{Effective height}}{\text{Effective thickness}}$$

BS 5628 Part 1: 1978 recommends that for walls
set in Portland cement mortars the slenderness ratio
should not exceed 20 for walls less than 90 mm thick
in buildings of more than two storeys and 27 in all
other cases. Table 6.7 gives reduction factors for
slenderness ratios from 0 to 27 for varying eccentricities at the top of the wall. Figure 6.3 illustrates
various assessments of eccentricities.

Table 6.7 Capacity reduction factor β

Slenderness ratio	*Eccentricity at top of wall*			
	Up to 0·05t	*0·1t*	*0·2t*	*0·3t*
0	1·00	0·88	0·66	0·44
6	1·00	0·88	0·66	0·44
8	1·00	0·88	0·66	0·44
10	0·97	0·88	0·66	0·44
12	0·93	0·87	0·66	0·44
14	0·89	0·83	0·66	0·44
16	0·83	0·77	0·64	0·44
18	0·77	0·70	0·57	0·44
20	0·70	0·64	0·51	0·37
22	0·62	0·56	0·43	0·30
24	0·53	0·47	0·34	
26	0·45	0·38		
27	0·40	0·33		

NOTE. It is not necessary to consider the effects of eccentricities up to and
including 0·05t.

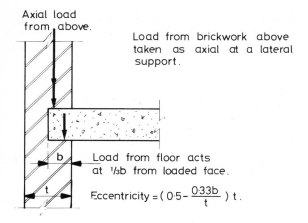

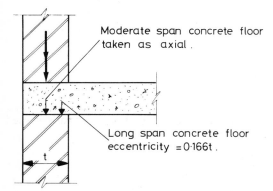

Figure 6.3   Assessment of eccentricity: typical examples

Design vertical load resistance of walls

This is given by

$\beta t f_k / \gamma_m$ per unit length of wall

where β = the capacity reduction factor allowing for the effects of slenderness and eccentricity (see Table 6.7), f_k = the characteristic strength of the masonry obtained from Table 6.1 or 6.2, t = the thickness of the wall and γ_m = the partial safety factor for the material obtained from Table 6.5.

Design vertical load resistance of columns

This is given by $\beta b t f_k / \gamma_m$

where f_k = the characteristic strength of the masonry obtained from Table 6.1 or 6.2, t = the

thickness of the column, b = the width of the column and β = the capacity reduction factor determined in accordance with the recommendations of BS 5628 Part 1: 1978.

Design vertical load resistance of cavity walls and columns

When the applied vertical load acts between the centroids of the two leaves of a cavity wall or walls, it should be replaced by two equivalent axial loads on the two leaves, and then designed in accordance with the above.

Concentrated loads (design stress reductions)
BS 5628 Part 1: 1978 suggests three types of concentrated load application where the normal design stress may be reduced.

Type 1. The stresses obtained from concentrated loads bearing over substantial areas of the wall (see Figure 6.4) may be increased by 1·25 times the normal design stress.

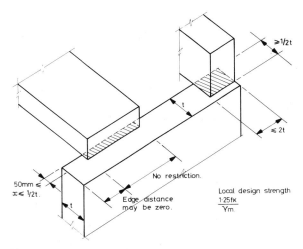

Figure 6.4   A typical concentrated load of type 1

Type 2. The stresses obtained from concentrated loads bearing over very limited areas of the wall (see Figure 6.5) may be increased by 1·50 times the normal design stress.
Type 3. The stresses obtained from concentrated loads borne by properly designed spreader beams located at the end of the wall (see Figure 6.6) may be increased by 2·0 times the normal design stress.

It should be remembered that all other loadings on the same area as the concentrated load must be taken into account in the design.

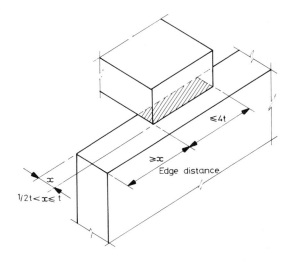

Local design strength $\dfrac{1.5f_K}{\gamma_m}$

Figure 6.5 A typical concentrated load of type 2

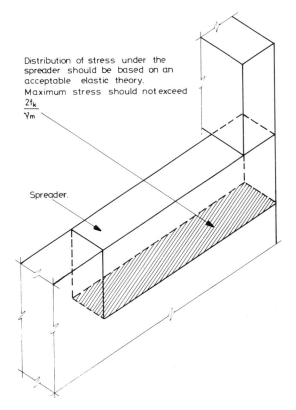

Distribution of stress under the spreader should be based on an acceptable elastic theory. Maximum stress should not exceed $\dfrac{2f_k}{\gamma_m}$

Spreader.

Figure 6.6 A typical concentrated load of type 3

Walls subjected to shear forces

BS 5628 Part 1: 1978 should be consulted where walls resist, in shear, horizontal forces acting in their plane.

6.2 EXAMPLES OF DETERMINING THE EFFECTIVE THICKNESS OF BRICK AND BLOCK WALLS

1. Determine the effective thickness for the unstiffened cavity wall shown in Figure 6.7.

Case (a) $t_{ef} = \frac{2}{3}(t_1 + t_2)$
$\qquad t_{ef} = \frac{2}{3}(150 + 75) = 150$ mm
Case (b) $t_{ef} = t_1 = 150$ mm
Case (c) $t_{ef} = t_2 = 75$ mm

In this example the effective thickness of the wall $=$ 150 mm.

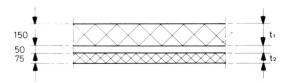

Figure 6.7 An unstiffened cavity wall

2. Determine the effective thickness for the stiffened single-leaf wall shown in Figure 6.8.

$$\frac{\text{Pier spacing}}{\text{Pier width}} = \frac{4400}{440} = 10$$

$$\frac{\text{Pier thickness}}{\text{Actual wall thickness}} = \frac{430}{215} = 2$$

From Table 6.6 stiffness coefficient $K = 1.2$
Hence $t_{ef} = 1.2t = 1.2 \times 215 = 258$ mm
Effective thickness of wall $= 258$ mm

3. Determine the effective thickness for the stiffened cavity wall shown in Figure 6.9.

$$\frac{\text{Pier spacing}}{\text{Pier width}} = \frac{4400}{440} = 10$$

$$\frac{\text{Pier thickness}}{\text{Actual wall thickness}} = \frac{215}{102.5} = 2.09$$

From Table 6.6 the stiffness coefficient $K = 1.22$ (by interpolation)
Hence $t_{1\,ef} = 1.22 \times 102.5 = 125.1$ mm
Therefore $t_{ef} = \frac{2}{3}(125.1 + 102.5) = 151.73$ mm

In this example the effective thickness of the wall $= 151.73$ mm.

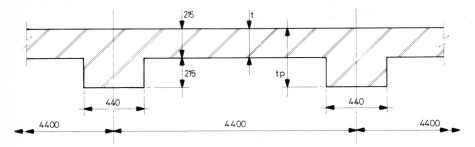

Figure 6.8   A stiffened single-leaf wall

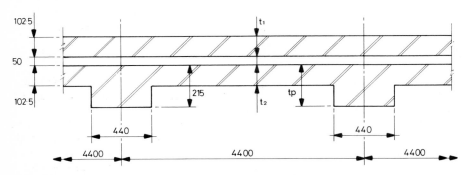

Figure 6.9   A stiffened cavity wall

6.3 DESIGN OF SIMPLE SINGLE-LEAF WALL

1. Estimate the characteristic loads G_k and Q_k (kN).
2. Calculate design loads using partial safety factors from Table 6.4.
3. Assess the type of lateral support at the top and bottom of the wall and determine the effective height (mm).
4. Calculate the effective thickness of the wall if necessary (mm).
5. Calculate the slenderness ratio of the wall from

$$\frac{\text{Effective height}}{\text{Effective thickness}}$$

6. Assess the degree of eccentricity of loading at the top of the wall.

7. Select the capacity reduction factor β from Table 6.7.
8. Select the partial safety factor for material strength γ_m from Table 6.5.
9. Calculate the characteristic compressive strength of the masonry from

$$f_k = \frac{\text{Design load} \times \gamma_m}{\beta \times t}$$

10. Select the appropriate mortar designation and type of mortar from Table 6.3.
11. Select the brick or block strength from Tables 6.1 or 6.2.

7 Retaining walls

For earth-retaining structures, the relevant code is Civil Engineering code of practice No. 2 (1951). It should be noted that some of the information contained in this publication is still in imperial units. It is, however, anticipated that the code will be revised and published as a British Standard at a future date.

7.1 PRESSURES ON RETAINING WALLS DUE TO SOIL AND OTHER GRANULAR MATERIALS

The pressures considered in this book apply to cohesionless soils such as sands and gravels. Other materials which possess the property of internal friction, e.g. coal, coke, grain and certain ores, may also be considered under this heading. Pressures due to cohesive soils such as silts and clays are too complex to be dealt with in a work of this description and reference should be made to the code.

Symbols used in calculating pressures on retaining walls

B breadth of the base or foundation of the wall

D depth of the foot of foundation below ground level at front of wall

d distance of a point below the earth surface in front of the wall

e eccentricity of the resultant thrust

f_1 pressure on the foundation soil at the toe of the wall

f_2 pressure on the foundation soil at the heel of the wall

H vertical height of the earth retained by the wall and foundation

h net vertical height of the earth retained by the wall

h_w vertical distance to ground water level

K_a coefficient of active earth pressure for cohesionless soils

L length generally

P_a total active lateral thrust per unit length of wall on the wall back due to earth alone

p_a intensity of active lateral pressure at a given depth due to earth alone

P_p total passive resistance of earth in front of the wall

p_p intensity of the passive resistance of the earth in front of the wall at a given depth below the surface

P_u total lateral thrust per unit length of wall on wall back due to uniformly distributed load

p_u intensity of lateral pressure at a given depth due to superimposed uniformly distributed surcharge

p_w intensity of water pressure on wall back at a given depth

q maximum safe bearing capacity of the soil

R resultant thrust on the foundation soil per unit length of wall

R_H horizontal component of the resultant thrust on the foundation soil per unit length of wall

R_v vertical component of the resultant thrust on the foundation soil per unit length of wall

W weight per unit length

W_s intensity of surcharge loading per unit area

z vertical distance measured behind the wall

γ_a average density of all the strata down to a given depth

γ_b submerged density of soil

γ_d dry density of soil

γ_m moist density of soil

γ_s saturated density of soil

γ_w density of water

δ angle of friction between the retained earth and the wall back

ϕ angle of internal friction of the retained earth.

7.2 ACTIVE PRESSURES ON A VERTICAL WALL WITH COHESIONLESS SOIL BACKING

(a) Horizontal ground (Figures 7.1 and 7.2)
The active pressure intensity at any depth below the horizontal ground surface is given by the equation

$$p_a = K_a \gamma z \sec \delta \ (kN/m^2)$$

The total active pressure

$$P_a = K_a \gamma \frac{H^2}{2} \sec \delta \ (kN/m)$$

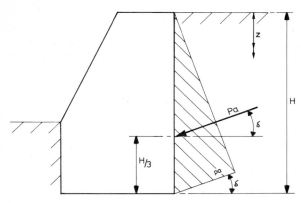

Figure 7.1 Active pressure diagram (general case)

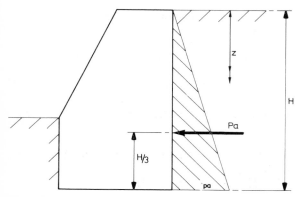

Figure 7.2 Active pressure diagram (Rankine)

Rankine's formula assumes that $\delta = 0$; therefore sec $0 = 1$ and hence

$p_a = K_a \gamma_z$ (kN/m²)
$P_a = K_a \gamma H^2/2$ (kN/m)
$K_a = \dfrac{1 - \sin \phi}{1 + \sin \phi} = \tan^2\left(45 - \dfrac{\phi}{2}\right)$

Typical values of ϕ and K_a are given in Tables 7.1 and 7.2. Densities of cohesionless materials are given in Table 7.3.

Table 7.1 Typical values of ϕ for cohesionless materials

Material	ϕ (degrees)
Sandy gravel	35–45
Compact sand	35–40
Loose sand	30–35
Shale filling	30–35
Rock filling	35–45
Ashes or broken brick	35–45

Table 7.2 Values of K_a for cohesionless materials for various values of δ and ϕ_λ (vertical walls and horizontal ground)

δ	ϕ				
	25°	*30°*	*35°*	*40°*	*45°*
0°	0·41	0·33	0·27	0·22	0·17
10°	0·37	0·31	0·25	0·20	0·16
20°	0·34	0·28	0·23	0·19	0·15
30°	–	0·26	0·21	0·17	0·14

Table 7.3 Densities* (kg/m³) of cohensionless materials

Material	γ_m	γ_b
Gravel	1600–2000 ⎫	
Coarse and medium sands	1680–2080 ⎬ 960–1280	
Fine and silty sands	1760–2160 ⎭	
Rocks		
granites and shales	1600–2080	960–1280
basalts and dolerites	1760–2240	1120–1600
limestones and sandstones	1280–1920	640–1280
chalk	960–1280	320–620
Broken brick	1120–1760	640–960
Ashes	640–960	320–480

γ_m = density when drained above ground water level.
γ_b = density when submerged below ground water level.
Fully saturated density = submerged density + 1000 kg/m³.
$\gamma_s = \gamma_b + \gamma_w$.

(b) Superimposed uniformly distributed load, horizontal ground (Figure 7.3)

Rankine replaced the superimposed uniformly distributed load by an equivalent height of earth;

Hence $h_e = W_s/\gamma$
where h_e = the equivalent height of earth, W_s = the superimposed uniformly distributed load, and γ = the density of material. The active pressure intensity

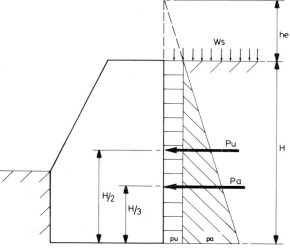

Figure 7.3 Active pressure and surcharge diagram

at any depth below the horizontal ground surface is therefore given by the equation

$$p_u = K_a \gamma h_e \text{ (kN/m}^2)$$

The total active pressure

$$P_u = K_a \gamma h_e H \text{ (kN/m)}$$

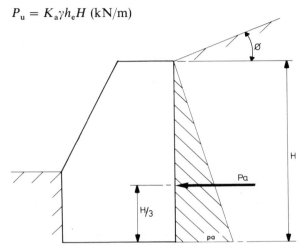

Figure 7.4 Active pressure diagram (Rankine) for inclined ground

(c) Ground sloping at an angle equal to the angle of repose (Figure 7.4)

In this case Rankine assumed that the angle of repose is equal to the angle of internal friction. Therefore the active pressure intensity at any depth is given by the equation

$$p_a = \gamma z \cos \phi \text{ (kN/m}^2)$$

The total active pressure

$$P_a = \gamma \frac{H^2}{2} \cos \phi \text{ (kN/m)}$$

However, another method which the student may consider for this case is Coulomb's wedge theory. Space does not allow a description here of the wedge theory, but it is fully described in most books on the mechanics of engineering soils.

(d) Saturated soils, horizontal ground (Figure 7.5)

If the ground water level is at a depth h_w below the surface of the ground, the backing will be water-logged below this level, and its density will be the submerged value as shown in Table 7.3. Rankine's formula then becomes

$$p_1 = K_a \gamma_m h_w \text{ (kN/m}^2)$$
$$P_1 = K_a \gamma_m h_w^2 / 2 \text{ (kN/m)} \qquad (1)$$
$$p_1 = K_a \gamma_m h_w \text{ (kN/m}^2)$$
$$P_2 = K_a \gamma_m h_w (H - h_w) \text{ (kN/m)} \qquad (2)$$
$$p_2 = K_a \gamma_b (H - h_w) \text{ (kN/m}^2)$$
$$P_3 = K_a \gamma_b \left(\frac{H - h_w}{2}\right)^2 \text{ (kN/m)} \qquad (3)$$
$$p_3 = \gamma_w (H - h_w) \text{ (kN/m}^2)$$
$$P_4 = \gamma_w \left(\frac{H - h_w}{2}\right)^2 \text{ (kN/m)} \qquad (4)$$

Hence total active pressure $= P_1 + P_2 + P_3 + P_4$

7.3 PASSIVE PRESSURES ON A VERTICAL WALL WITH COHESIONLESS SOIL

(a) *Horizontal ground* (Figures 7.6 and 7.7)

The intensity of passive resistance at any depth below the horizontal ground surface is given by the equation

$$p_p = K_p \gamma d \sec \delta \text{ (kN/m}^2)$$

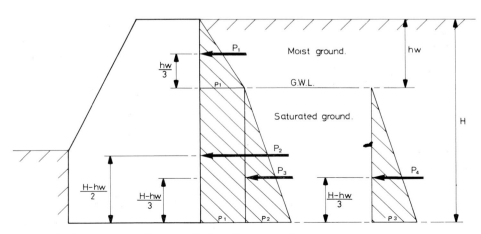

Figure 7.5 Active pressure diagrams (Rankine) for saturated ground

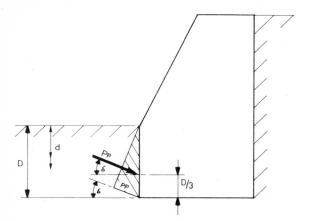

Figure 7.6   Passive pressure diagram (general case)

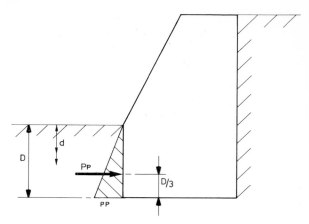

Figure 7.7   Passive pressure diagram (Rankine)

Figure 7.8   Passive pressure diagrams (Rankine) for saturated ground

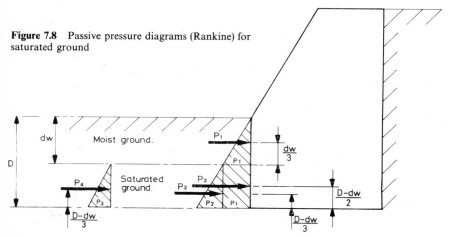

Total passive resistance

$$P_p = (K_p \gamma d^2)2/\sec \delta \, (kN/m)$$

As before, Rankine's formula assumes that $\delta = 0$; hence

$$p_p = K_p \gamma d \, (kN/m^2)$$
$$P_p = K_p \gamma D^2/2 \, (kN/m)$$
$$K_p = \frac{1 + \sin \phi}{1 - \sin \phi} = \tan^2\left(45 + \frac{\phi}{2}\right)$$

Table 7.4   Values of K_p for cohesionless materials for various values of δ and ϕ (vertical walls and horizontal ground)

δ	ϕ			
	25°	*30°*	*35°*	*40°*
0°	2·5	3·0	3·7	4·6
10°	3·1	4·0	4·8	6·5
20°	3·7	4·9	6·0	8·8
30°	–	5·8	7·3	11·4

Table 7.5   Maximum safe bearing capacities for foundations of width greater than 1 m and depth not less than 600 mm (cohesionless soils)

Type of soil	*Typical values of ϕ (degrees)*	*Max safe bearing capacity (kN/m²)*	
		Dry*	*Submerged*
Compact well-graded sands and gravel–sand mixtures	40–45	400–600	200–300
Loose well-graded sands and gravel–sand mixtures	35–40	200–400	100–200
Compact uniform sands	35–40	200–400	100–200
Loose uniform sands	30–35	100–200	50–100

* 'Dry' means that the ground water level is at a depth not less than the width (of *B*) of the foundation below the bottom of the foundation.

Typical values of K_p are given in Table 7.4.
(b) *Saturated soils, horizontal ground* (Figure 7.8)
In this case, using Rankine's formula

$$p_1 = K_p\gamma_m d_w \ (\text{kN/m}^2)$$
$$P_1 = K_p\gamma_m d_w^2/2 \ (\text{kN/m}) \tag{1}$$

$$p_1 = K_p\gamma_m d_w \ (\text{kN/m}^2)$$
$$P_2 = K_p\gamma_m d_w(D - d_w) \ (\text{kN/m}) \tag{2}$$

$$p_2 = K_p\gamma_b(D - d_w) \ (\text{kN/m}^2)$$
$$P_3 = K_p\gamma_b\left(\frac{D - d_w}{2}\right)^2 \ (\text{kN/m}) \tag{3}$$

$$p_3 = \gamma_w(D - d_w) \ (\text{kN/m}^2)$$
$$P_4 = \gamma_w\left(\frac{D - d_w}{2}\right)^2 \ (\text{kN/m}) \tag{4}$$

Hence total passive resistance $= P_1 + P_2 + P_3 + P_4$

7.4 BEARING PRESSURES ON FOUNDATION SOIL

The bearing pressures on the foundation soil beneath the base of the wall may be calculated as follows:

(a) where R_v falls inside the middle third of the base

$$f_1 = \frac{R_v}{B}\left(1 + \frac{6e}{B}\right)$$
$$f_2 = \frac{R_v}{B}\left(1 - \frac{6e}{B}\right)$$

(b) Where R_v falls at the middle third of the base

$$f_1 = 2R_v/B$$
$$f_2 = 0$$

(c) Where R_v falls outside the middle third of the base

$$f_1 = \frac{2R_v}{3b}$$
$$f_2 = 0$$

The assumed distributions of bearing pressure for the above cases are shown in Figure 7.9. The maximum pressure f in all cases should not exceed the maximum safe bearing capacity of the soil. Typical values for cohesionless soils are given in Table 7.5.

It should be noted that in gravity walls R_v should not fall outside the middle third of the base.

7.5 DESIGN OF A GRAVITY WALL WITH COHESIONLESS SOIL BACKING AND HORIZONTAL GROUND. $\delta = 0$

1. Assume a cross section for the wall (width of base approximately half the height of wall).

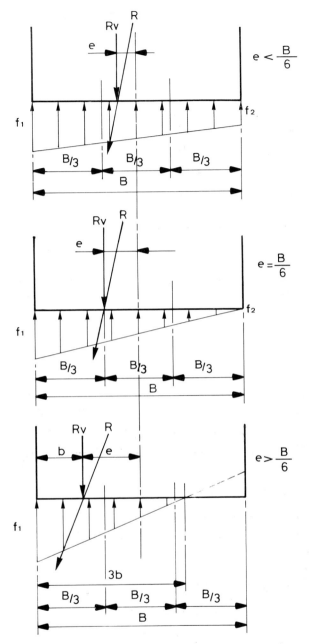

Figure 7.9 Bearing pressure diagrams

2. Calculate the vertical line in which the centroid lies by taking moments of areas about the back of the wall (Figure 7.10).
3. Calculate the weight W of one metre run of wall and the total active pressure P due to the earth backing.
4. Find graphically or by calculation where the resultant thrust R of P_a and W cuts the base of the wall and determine the eccentricity e. Graphically,

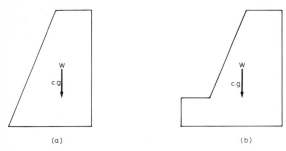

Figure 7.10   The centre of gravity of retaining walls

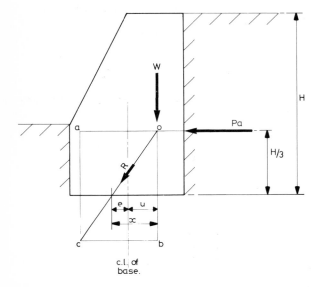

Figure 7.11   The position of the resultant thrust in a gravity wall

and with reference to Figure 7.11, to scale Oa represents P_a, Ob represents W and Oc is the resultant thrust R. Hence e can be obtained by scaling the distance from the mid-point of the base to the point where the resultant cuts the base of the wall.

By calculation $x = \dfrac{P_a H}{3W}$ $e = x - u$

where u = the distance from the centre of gravity of the wall to the mid-point of the base.

5. Calculate the bearing pressures on the foundation soil beneath the base (see 7.4).

7.6 DESIGN OF A REINFORCED CONCRETE CANTILEVER WALL WITH COHESIONLESS SOIL BACKING AND HORIZONTAL GROUND. $\delta = 0$

1. Assume dimensions for the base and stem. The thickness of the base should be at least equal to the thickness of the stem. The width B of the base is about $\frac{2}{3}$ the height of the wall for Figure 7.12(a) and about $\frac{1}{2}$ the height of the wall for Figures 7.12(b) and 7.12(c).
2. Calculate the total ultimate active pressure P_a due to earth backing. It should be noted that the pressure acts horizontally ($\delta = 0$) in the case of reinforced concrete retaining walls.
3. Calculate the vertical line in which the centroid lies, by taking moments of areas about the heel of the wall (Figure 7.13).

W_S = weight of stem per metre run (kN)
W_B = weight of base per metre run (kN)
W_E = weight of earth per metre run (kN)

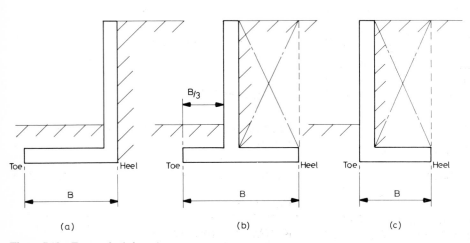

Figure 7.12   Types of reinforced concrete cantilever walls

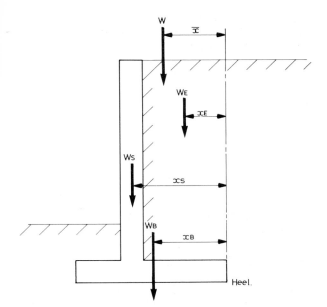

Figure 7.13 The position of the resultant load in a reinforced concrete cantilever wall

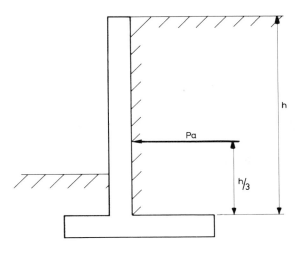

$$M \text{ at bottom of stem} = \frac{Pah}{3}$$

Figure 7.14 The moment in the stem of a reinforced concrete cantilever wall

Taking moments about heel

$$(W_S + W_B + W_E)\bar{x} = W_S x_S + W_B x_B + W_E x_E$$

4. Calculate the weight of one metre run of wall. Hence $W = W_S + W_B + W_E$.
5. Find where the resultant thrust (R) of P_a and W cuts the base (as for gravity walls).
6. Calculate the bearing pressures on the foundation soil beneath the base (see 7.4).
7. Calculate the ultimate bending moment in the stem (Figure 7.14) and determine the amount of reinforcement required in accordance with CP 110: 1972.
8. Calculate the ultimate bending moments in the base; i.e. the ultimate bending moment at XX in Figure 7.15 is due to downward pressure of earth, downward pressure due to weight of base, and upward pressure due to reaction from soil. Calculate the reinforcement required. Moment and reinforcement calculations should be in accordance with CP 110: 1972.

7.7 FACTORS OF SAFETY FOR RETAINING WALLS IN COHESIONLESS MATERIALS

(i) Resistance to overturning (Figure 7.16)
In gravity walls the resultant thrust should not fall outside the middle third of the base of the wall. In

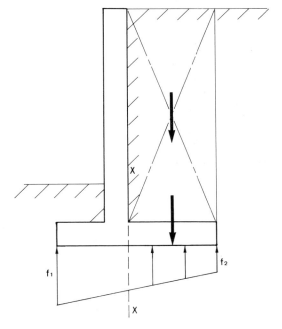

Figure 7.15 The moment in the base of a reinforced concrete cantilever wall

all other cases a factor of safety of at least 2 is required.

(ii) Bearing pressures
The maximum pressure exerted on the foundation

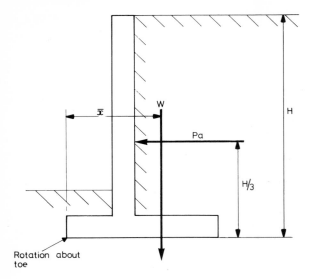

Rotation about
toe

For walls other than the gravity type.

Factor of safety $= \dfrac{\text{Stabilising moment}}{\text{Overturning moment}}$

$\qquad = \dfrac{W\bar{x}}{Pa\,H/3} = \dfrac{3W\bar{x}}{PaH} \geqslant 2$

Figure 7.16   Resistance to overturning of a reinforced concrete cantilever wall

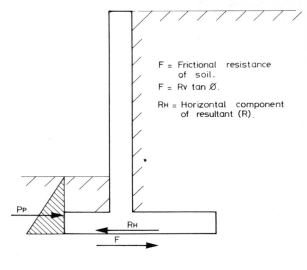

Factor of safety $= \dfrac{F + Pp}{R_H} \geqslant 2$

Figure 7.17   Resistance to forward movement of a reinforced concrete cantilever wall

soil beneath the wall base, which will usually be at the toe, should not exceed the safe bearing capacity appropriate to the foundation soil. For typical values of safe bearing capacities see Table 7.5. These give a factor of safety of at least 2.

(iii) Resistance to forward movement (sliding) (Figure 7.17)

For cohesionless soils, the base friction resistance under a concrete foundation cast *in situ* may be determined by assuming that the angle of friction beneath the base is equal to the tangent of the angle of internal friction of the soil beneath the foundation (see Table 7.17). When the foundation is not cast *in situ*, the angle of friction should be taken as equal to δ, the angle of wall friction.

In theory the passive pressure will assist in resisting the forward moment of the wall, due to active pressure. This should be treated with extreme caution as the passive resistance of the ground is often sought at relatively shallow depths where the soil is subject to seasonal change.

In computing the total force resisting sliding, base friction or adhesion may be added to the passive resistance of the ground in front of the toe. A factor of safety of approximately 2 should be applied to the total force calculations.